Stories
about Sets

ACADEMIC PAPERBACKS*

EDITED BY Henry Booker, D. Allan Bromley, Nicholas DeClaris, W. Magnus, Alvin Nason, and A. Shenitzer

BIOLOGY

Design and Function at the Threshold of Life: The Viruses
HEINZ FRAENKEL-CONRAT
The Evolution of Genetics ARNOLD W. RAVIN
Isotopes in Biology GEORGE WOLF
Life: Its Nature, Origin, and Development A. I. OPARIN
Time, Cells, and Aging BERNARD L. STREHLER
The Spread of Cancer JOSEPH LEIGHTON

ENGINEERING

A Vector Approach to Oscillations HENRY BOOKER
Dynamic Programming and Modern Control Theory RICHARD BELLMAN and ROBERT KALABA
Hamilton's Principle and Physical Systems B. R. GOSSICK

MATHEMATICS

Finite Permutation Groups HELMUT WIELANDT
Complex Numbers in Geometry I. M. YAGLOM
Elements of Abstract Harmonic Analysis GEORGE BACHMAN
Geometric Transformations (in two volumes) P. S. MODENOV and A. S. PARKHOMENKO
Introduction to p-Adic Numbers and Valuation Theory GEORGE BACHMAN
Linear Operators in Hilbert Space WERNER SCHMEIDLER
The Method of Averaging Functional Corrections: Theory and Applications A. Yu. LUCHKA
Noneuclidean Geometry HERBERT MESCHKOWSKI
Quadratic Forms and Matrices N. V. YEFIMOV
Representation Theory of Finite Groups MARTIN BURROW
Stories about Sets N. Ya. VILENKIN
Commutative Matrices D. A. SUPRUNENKO and R. I. TYSHKEVICH

PHYSICS

Crystals: Their Role in Nature and in Science CHARLES BUNN
Elementary Dynamics of Particles H. W. HARKNESS
Elementary Plane Rigid Dynamics H. W. HARKNESS
Mössbauer Effect: Principles and Applications GUNTHER K. WERTHEIM
Potential Barriers in Semiconductors B. R. GOSSICK
Principles of Vector Analysis JERRY B. MARION

*Most of these volumes are also available in a cloth bound edition.

STORIES
ABOUT SETS

N. Ya. Vilenkin

Translated by SCRIPTA TECHNICA

ACADEMIC PRESS New York and London

ACADEMIC PRESS, INC.
111 Fifth Avenue, New York, New York 10003

United Kingdom Edition published by
ACADEMIC PRESS, INC. (LONDON) LTD.
Berkeley Square House, London W.1

LIBRARY OF CONGRESS CATALOG CARD NUMBER: 66-30111

Third Printing August, 1970
Fourth Printing December, 1970

PRINTED IN THE UNITED STATES OF AMERICA

First published in the Russian language under the title

RASSKAZY O MNOZHESTVAKH

by

IZDATEL'STVO "NAUKA"
GLAVNAYA REDAKTSIYA FIZIKO-MATEMATICHESKOĬ LITERATURY
Moscow, 1965

Foreword

Professor Vilenkin has produced a small masterpiece which can be read with profit and delight by anybody, beginning with high school juniors and seniors. Slightly more than half of the book explores the notion of cardinality of sets and the remainder traces the evolution of some of the most important concepts of mathematics such as function, curve, surface, and dimension. The exposition combines informality with integrity of presentation and there is a wealth of unusual examples illustrating the paradoxical properties of curves and surfaces. It is safe to say that Professor Vilenkin's essay provides a royal road to the important concepts with which it is concerned.

A. SHENITZER

January, 1968
Adelphi University
Garden City, New York

v

Preface

I first had occasion to hear of the theory of sets at a lecture conducted by I. M. Gel'fand for Moscow school children. He was then just beginning his teaching career, but is now a corresponding member of the Academy of Sciences of the USSR. During the course of two hours he told us about what seemed to us to be completely improbable things: that there are just as many natural numbers as there are rational numbers, and that there are just as many points in an interval as there are in a square.

My acquaintance with the theory of sets was further developed during my time as a student of mathematics and mechanics at the Moscow State University. In addition to the lectures and seminars, we had our own ways of learning, ways that our professors and lecturers probably did not even suspect. After class (and sometimes, I must confess, even during class, if the lecture was not especially interesting) we wandered through the corridors of the old building on Mokhovoi Street and discussed interesting problems, surprising examples, and clever proofs. In these conversations, for example, the first-year students learned from their more experienced fellows how to construct a curve which passes through all the points of a square, or how to find a function which has a derivative nowhere, and so forth.

Of course, the explanations given were, so to speak, "out of bounds," and it would be considered a mark of inexcusable frivolousness if you went to take an exam after having listened to these discussions. No, really, there was no talk of exams—according to the course of study, we would not be taking "real variables" for two more years. But, then, how this "corridor" preparation helped in taking exams and understanding lectures! For each of the theorems we could recall interesting problems which we had to solve earlier, perceptive juxtapositions, and intuitive examples.

I want to tell the reader about the theory of sets in the same way, in which I learned it, by following the "corridor" course of study. Thus, our attention will be focused mainly on giving clear presentations of problems, discussing unexpected or surprising examples, quite often giving contradictory "naive" discussions. We shall find that the theory of functions of a real variable is richly endowed with all these. And if, after he has read this book, a high-school or college student wants to study the theory of sets or the theory of functions of a real variable more deeply, the author will feel that his book has been a success.

Of the many standard presentations of these subjects, the following are recommended:

1. A. N. Kolmogorov and S. V. Fomin, "Measure, Lebesgue Integrals, and Hilbert Space" (Book II of "Elements of the Theory of Functions and Functional Analysis," translated by N. A. Brunswick and A. Jeffrey). Academic Press, New York, 1961.

2. I. P. Natanson, "Theory of Functions of a Real Variable," Vol. 1, edited by Leo F. Boron and Edwin Hewitt, 1955. Vol. 2, edited by Leo F. Boron, 1959. Ungar, New York.

3. F. Hausdorff, "Set Theory," 2nd ed.   Chelsea, New York, 1967.

Much interesting information about some of the problems touched upon here can be found in the book of A. S. Parkhomenko "Chto takoe liniya."

Some problems from the theory of functions of a real variable are given at the end of the book; the reader will find it helpful to attempt their solution.

Contents

4. Remarkable Functions and Curves, or a Stroll through a Mathematical Art Museum

1

Some Extraordinary Properties of Infinite Sets

It would not be an exaggeration to say that all of mathematics derives from the concept of infinity. In mathematics, as a rule, we are not interested in individual objects (numbers, geometric figures), but in whole classes of such objects: *all* natural numbers, *all* triangles, and so on. But such a collection consists of an *infinite* number of individual objects.

For this reason mathematicians and philosophers have always been interested in the concept of infinity. This interest arose at the very moment when it became clear that each natural number has a successor, i.e., that the number sequence is infinite. However, even the first attempts to cope with infinity lead to numerous paradoxes.

For example, the Greek philosopher Zeno used the concept of infinity to prove that motion was impossible! Indeed, he said, for an arrow to reach its target it must first cover half the distance to the target. But before it can cover this half, it has to cover a fourth, an eighth, etc. Since the process of halving is a never-ending one (here infinity crops up!), the arrow never leaves the bow. He proved in an identical fashion that swift Achilles never overtakes the slow tortoise.

Fig. 1.   Achilles and the tortoise.

Because of these paradoxes and sophisms, the ancient Greek mathematicians refused to have anything to do with the notion of infinity and excluded it from their mathematical arguments. They assumed that all geometric figures consisted of a finite number of minute, indivisible parts (atoms). With this assumption, it turned out to be impossible, for instance, to divide the circle into two equal parts—the center would have to belong to one of the two parts, but this would contradict their equality.

In the Middle Ages the problem of infinity was of interest mainly in connection with arguments about whether the set of angels who could sit on the head of a pin was infinite or not. A wider use of the notion of infinity began in the 17th century, when mathematical analysis was founded. Concepts such as "infinitely large quantity" and "infinitely small quantity" were used in mathematical reasoning at every step. However, sets containing infinitely many elements were not studied at this time; what were studied were quantities which varied in such a way as eventually to become larger than any given number. Such quantities

FIG. 2. How many angels can sit on the head of a pin?

were called "potentially infinitely large," meaning that they could become as large as you please (potentia: possibility).

It was only in the middle of the 19th century that the study of infinite sets, consisting of an infinitely large number of elements, began to occur in the analysis of the concept

of infinity.   The founders of the mathematical theory of
infinite sets were the Czech savant B. Bolzano (unfortunately,
his main work was not published until many years after
his death in 1848) and the German mathematician Georg
Cantor. It is a curious fact that both founders of the theory
of sets were well acquainted with the science of the Scholastics. But they were able to improve on the Scholastics and
turn the theory of sets into an important part of mathematics.

The chief attainment of Bolzano and Cantor was the
study of the properties of infinite sets; the properties of
finite sets were well known by their predecessors. It turned
out that the properties of finite and infinite sets were
completely dissimilar: many operations impossible for
finite sets could be carried out with ease for infinite sets.
For example, try to find room in an already full hotel for
an additional guest, if it is assumed that each room cannot
have more than one occupant. It can't be done? This is
only because the number of rooms in a hotel is finite! But
if there were an infinite number of rooms. . . . Such hotels
can be found in the stories about the interstellar
traveler Ion the Quiet, the famous hero of "The Interstellar
Milkman, Ion the Quiet," written by the Polish fantasist
Stanislaw Lem. Let's hear what he has to say.

The Extraordinary Hotel, or the Thousand and First Journey of Ion the Quiet

I got home rather late—the get-together at the club
Andromeda Nebula dragged on long after midnight. I was
tormented by nightmares the whole night. I dreamt that
I had swallowed an enormous Kurdl; then I dreamt that
I was again on the planet Durditov and didn't know how
to escape one of those terrible machines they have there

that turn people into hexagons; then . . . . People generally advise against mixing old age with seasoned mead. An unexpected telephone call brought me back to reality. It was my old friend and companion in interstellar travels Professor Tarantog.

"A pressing problem, my dear Ion," I heard. "Astronomers have discovered a strange object in the cosmos—a mysterious black line stretching from one galaxy to another. No one knows what is going on. Even the best telescopes and radio-telescopes placed on rockets cannot help in unraveling the mystery. You are our last hope. Fly right away in the direction of nebula ACD-1587."

The next day I got my old photon rocket back from the repair shop and installed in it my time accelerator and my electronic robot who knows all the languages of the cosmos and all the stories about interstellar travel (it is guaranteed to keep me entertained for at least a five year journey). Then I took off to attend to the matter at hand.

Just as the robot exhausted his entire supply of stories and had begun to repeat himself (nothing is worse than listening to an electronic robot repeating an old story for the tenth time), the goal of my journey appeared in the distance. The galaxies which covered up the mysterious line lay behind me, and in front of me was . . . the hotel Cosmos. Some time ago I constructed a small planet for wandering interstellar exiles, but they tore this apart and again were without a refuge. After that, they decided to give up wandering into foreign galaxies and to put up a grandiose building—a hotel for all travelers in the cosmos. This hotel extended across almost all the galaxies. I say "almost all" because the exiles dismantled a few uninhabited galaxies and made off with a few poorly situated constellations from each of the remaining ones.

But they did a marvelous job of building the hotel. In each room there were faucets from which hot and cold plasma flowed. If you wished, you could be split into atoms for the night, and in the morning the porter would put your atoms back together again.

But, most important of all, there was an *infinite number of rooms* in the hotel. The exiles hoped that from now on no one would have to hear that irksome phrase that had plagued them during their time of wandering: "no room available."

In spite of this I had no luck. The first thing that caught my eye when I entered the vestibule of the hotel was a sign: Delegates to the cosmic zoologists' congress are to register on the 127th floor.

Since cosmic zoologists came from all the galaxies and there are an infinite number of these, it turned out that all the rooms were occupied by participants in the conference. There was no place for me. The manager tried, it is true, to get some of the delegates to agree to double up so that I could share a room with one of them. But when I found out that one proposed roommate breathed fluorine and another considered it normal to have the temperature of his environment at about 860°, I politely turned down such "pleasant" neighbors.

Luckily the director of the hotel had been an exile and well remembered the good turn I had done him and his fellows. He would try to find me a place at the hotel. After all, you could catch pneumonia spending the night in interstellar space. After some meditation, he turned to the manager and said:

"Put him in number 1."

"Where am I going to put the guest in number 1?"

"Put him in number 2. Shift the guest in number 2 to number 3, number 3 to number 4, and so on."

It was only at this point that I began to appreciate the unusual qualities of the hotel. If there had been only a finite number of rooms, the guest in the last room would have had to move out into interstellar space. But because the hotel had infinitely many rooms, there was space for all, and I was able to move in without depriving any of the cosmic zoologists of his room.

The following morning, I was not astonished to find that I was asked to move into number 1,000,000. It was simply that some cosmic zoologists had arrived belatedly from galaxy VSK-3472, and they had to find room for another 999,999 guests. But while I was going to the manager to pay for my room on the third day of my stay at the hotel, I was dismayed to see that from the manager's window there extended a line whose end disappeared somewhere near the clouds of Magellan. Just then I heard a voice:

"I will exchange two stamps from the Andromeda nebula for a stamp from Sirius."

"Who has the stamp Erpean from the 57th year of the cosmic era?"

I turned in bewilderment to the manager and asked:

"Who are these people?"
"This is the interstellar congress of philatelists."
"Are there many of them?"
"An infinite set—one representative from each galaxy."
"But how will you find room for them; after all, the cosmic zoologists don't leave till tomorrow?"

"I don't know; I am on my way now to speak to the director about it for a few minutes."

However, this time the problem turned out to be much more difficult and the few minutes extended into an hour. Finally, the manager left the office of the director and proceeded to make his arrangements. First he asked the guest in number 1 to move to number 2. This seemed strange to me, since I knew from my own experience that such a shift would only free one room, whereas he had to find places for nothing less than an infinite set of philatelists. But the manager continued to give orders:

"Put the guest from number 2 into number 4, the one from number 3 into number 6; in general, put the guest from number n into number $2n$."

Now his plan became clear: by this scheme he would free the infinite set of odd-numbered rooms and would be able to settle the philatelists in them. So in the end the even numbers turned out to be occupied by cosmic zoologists and the odd numbers by philatelists. (I didn't say anything about myself—after three days of acquaintance I became so friendly with the cosmic zoologists that I had been chosen an honorary representative to their congress; so I had to abandon my own room along with all the cosmic zoologists and move from number 1,000,000 to number 2,000,000). And a philatelist friend of mine who was 574th in line got room number 1147. In general, the philatelist who was nth in line got room number $2n - 1$.

The following day the room situation eased up—the cosmic zoologists' congress ended and they took off for home. I moved in with the director, in whose apartment there was a vacant room. But what is good for the guests does not always please the management. After a few days my generous host became sad.

"What's the trouble?" I asked him.
"Half the rooms are empty. We won't fulfill the financial plan."

Actually, I was not quite sure what financial plan he was talking about; after all, he was getting the fee for an infinite number of rooms, but I nevertheless gave him some advice:

"Well, why don't you move the guests closer together; move them around so as to fill all the rooms."

This turned out to be easy to do. The philatelists occupied only the odd rooms: 1, 3, 5, 7, 9, etc. They left the guest in number 1 alone. They moved number 3 into number 2, number 5 into number 3, number 7 into number 4, etc. At the end all the rooms were once again filled and not even one new guest had arrived.

But this did not end the director's unhappiness. It was explained that the exiles did not content themselves with the erection of the hotel Cosmos. The indefatigable builders then went on to construct an infinite set of hotels, each of which had infinitely many rooms. To do this they dismantled so many galaxies that the intergalactic equilibrium was upset and this could entail serious consequences. They were therefore asked to close all the hotels except ours and put the material used back into place. But it was difficult to carry out this order when all the hotels (ours included) were filled. He was asked to move all the guests from infinitely many hotels, each of which had infinitely many guests, into one hotel, and this one was already filled!

"I've had enough!" the director shouted. "First I put up one guest in an already full hotel, then another 999,999, then even an infinite set of guests; and now they want me to find room in it for an additional infinite set of infinite sets of guests. No, the hotel isn't made of rubber; let them put them where they want."

But an order was an order, and they had five days to get ready for the arrival of the new guests. Nobody worked in the hotel during these five days—everybody was pondering how to solve the problem. A contest was announced—the prize would be a tour of one of the galaxies. But all the solutions proposed were turned down as unsuccessful. Then a cook in training made the following proposal: leave the guest in number 1 in his present quarters, move number 2 into number 1001, number 3 into number 2001, etc. After this, put the guest from the second hotel into numbers 2, 1002, 2002, etc. of our hotel, the guests from the third hotel into numbers 3, 1003, 2003, etc. The project was turned down, for it was not clear where the guest of the 1001st hotel were to be placed; after all, the guests from the first 1000 hotels would occupy all the rooms. We recalled on this occasion that when the servile Roman senate offered to rename the month of September "Tiberius" to honor the emperor (the preceding months had already been given the names of Julius and Augustus), Tiberius asked them caustically "and what will you offer the thirteenth Caesar?"

The hotel's bookkeeper proposed a pretty good variant. He advised us to make use of the properties of the geometric progression and resettle the guests as follows: the guests from the first hotel are to be put in rooms 2, 4, 8, 16, 32, etc. (these numbers form a geometric progression with multiplier 2). The guests from the second hotel are to be put in rooms

3, 9, 27, 81, etc. (these are the terms of the geometric progression with multiplier 3). He proposed that we resettle the guests from the other hotels in a similar manner. But the director asked him:

"And we are to use the progression with multiplier 4 for the third hotel?"

"Of course," the bookkeeper replied.

"Then nothing is accomplished; after all, we already have someone from the first hotel in room 4, so where are we going to put the people from the third hotel?"

My turn to speak came; it was not for nothing that they made you study mathematics for five years at the Stellar Academy.

"Use prime numbers. Put the guests from the first hotel into numbers 2, 4, 8, 16, ..., from the second hotel into numbers 3, 9, 27, 81, ..., from the third into numbers 5, 25, 125, 625,..., the fourth into numbers 7, 49, 343,..."

"And it won't happen again that some room will have two guests?" the director asked.

"No. After all, if you take two prime numbers, none of their positive integer powers can equal one another. If p and q are prime numbers, $p \neq q$, and m and n are natural numbers, then $p^m \neq q^n$."

The director agreed with me and immediately found an improvement on the method I had proposed, in which only the primes 2 and 3 were needed. Namely, he proposed to put the guest from the mth room of the nth hotel into room number $2^m 3^n$. This works because if $m \neq p$ or $n \neq q$, $2^m 3^n \neq 2^p 3^q$. So no room would have two occupants.

This proposal delighted everyone. It was a solution of the problem that everyone had supposed insoluble. But neither the director nor I got the prize; too many rooms would be left unoccupied if our solutions were adopted (according to mine—such rooms as 6, 10, 12, and, more generally, all rooms whose numbers were not powers of primes, and according to the director's—all rooms whose numbers could not be written in the form 2^n3^m). The best solution was proposed by one of the philatelists, the president of the Academy of Mathematics of the galaxy Swan.

He proposed that we construct a tabulation, in whose rows the number of the hotel would appear, and in whose columns the room numbers would appear. For example, at the intersection of the 4th row and the 6th column there would appear the 6th room of the 4th hotel. Here is the tabulation (actually, only its upper left part, for to write down the entire tabulation we would have to employ infinitely many rows and columns):

$$
\begin{array}{cccccccc}
(1,1) & (1,2) & (1,3) & (1,4) & (1,5) & \ldots & (1,n) & \ldots \\[2mm]
(2,1) & (2,2) & (2,3) & (2,4) & (2,5) & \ldots & (2,n) & \ldots \\[2mm]
(3,1) & (3,2) & (3,3) & (3,4) & (3,5) & \ldots & (3,n) & \ldots \\[2mm]
(4,1) & (4,2) & (4,3) & (4,4) & (4,5) & \ldots & (4,n) & \ldots \quad (1.1) \\[2mm]
(5,1) & (5,2) & (5,3) & (5,4) & (5,5) & \ldots & (5,n) & \ldots \\[2mm]
 & & & & \vdots & & \vdots & \\[2mm]
(m,1) & (m,2) & (m,3) & (m,4) & (m,5) & \ldots & (m,n) & \ldots \\[2mm]
 & & & & \vdots & & \vdots & \\
\end{array}
$$

"And now settle the guests according to squares," the mathematician-philatelist said.

"How?" The director did not understand.

"By squares. In number 1 put the guest from $(1,1)$, i.e., from the first room of the first hotel; in number 2 put the guest from (1, 2), i.e., from the second room of the first hotel; in number 3 put the guest from (2, 2), the second room of the second hotel, and in number 4—the guest from (2, 1), the first room of the second hotel. We will thus have settled the guests from the upper left square of side 2. After this, put the guest from (1, 3) in number 5, from (2, 3) in number 6, from (3, 3) in number 7, from (3, 2) in number 8, from (3, 1) in number 9. (These rooms fill the square of side 3.) And we carry on in this way:

$$
\begin{array}{cccccccc}
(1,1) & (1,2) & (1,3) & (1,4) & (1,5) & \ldots & (1,n) & \ldots \\
& \downarrow & \downarrow & \downarrow & \downarrow & & \downarrow & \\
(2,1) \leftarrow & (2,2) & (2,3) & (2,4) & (2,5) & \ldots & (2,n) & \ldots \\
& & \downarrow & \downarrow & \downarrow & & \downarrow & \\
(3,1) \leftarrow & (3,2) \leftarrow & (3,3) & (3,4) & (3,5) & \ldots & (3,n) & \ldots \\
& & & \downarrow & \downarrow & & \downarrow & \\
(4,1) \leftarrow & (4,2) \leftarrow & (4,3) \leftarrow & (4,4) & (4,5) & \ldots & (4,n) & \ldots \\
& & & & \downarrow & & \downarrow & \\
(5,1) \leftarrow & (5,2) \leftarrow & (5,3) \leftarrow & (5,4) \leftarrow & (5,5) & \ldots & (5,n) & \ldots \\
& & & & & \vdots & \downarrow & \vdots \\
(n,1) \leftarrow & (n,2) \leftarrow & (n,3) \leftarrow & (n,4) \leftarrow & (n,5) \leftarrow & \ldots & (n,n) & \ldots \\
& & & & & \vdots & & \vdots
\end{array}
$$

$$(1.2)$$

"Will there really be enough room for all?" The director was doubtful.

"Of course. After all, according to this scheme we settle the guests from the first n rooms of the first n hotels in the first n^2 rooms. So sooner or later every guest will get a room. For example, if we are talking about the guest from number 136 in hotel number 217, he will get a room at the 217th stage. We can even easily figure out which room. It will have the number $216^2 + 136$. More generally, if the guest occupies room n in the mth hotel, then if $n \geq m$ he will occupy number $(n-1)^2 + m$, and if $n < m$, number $m^2 - n + 1$."

The proposed project was recognized to be the best—all the guests from all hotels would find a place in our hotel, and not even one room would be empty. The mathematician-philatelist received the prize—a tour of galaxy LCR-287.

In honor of this so successful solution, the director organized a reception to which he invited all the guests. The reception, too, had its problems. The occupants of the even-numbered rooms arrived a half hour late, and when they appeared, it turned out that all the chairs were occupied, even though our kind host had arranged to have a chair for each guest. They had to wait while everyone shifted to new places so as to free the necessary quantity of seats (of course, not one new chair was brought into the hall). Later on when they began to serve ice cream to the guests, it was discovered that each guest had two portions, although, as a matter of fact, the cook had only prepared one portion per guest. I hope that by now the reader can figure out by himself how this happened.

At the end of the reception I got into my photon rocket and took off for Earth. I had to inform the cosmonauts of Earth about the new haven existing in the cosmos. Besides, I wanted to consult some of the prominent mathematicians and my friend Professor Tarantog about the properties of infinite sets.

From the Author

With this we take leave temporarily of our hero. Many of his stories give rise to doubt—after all, according to the laws of the theory of relativity it is impossible to transmit signals at speeds greater than 186,000 miles/sec. Thus, even the very first order of the director would require infinitely many intervals of time to carry out. But let us not ask too much of Ion the Quiet—he has had even more improbable adventures during his travels.

The rest of the book is devoted to the story of the theory of sets. And although the events will no longer take place in interstellar space but on the interval [0, 1] or the square of side 1, many of them will seem no less unusual.

2

Sets and Operations on Sets

What Do We Mean by a Set?

Before we can discuss the properties of infinite sets, we have to become acquainted with the meaning of the term *set* and the kind of operations that can be carried out on sets. Unfortunately, we are not in a position to give a rigorous definition of the fundamental concept of the theory: the concept of set. Of course, we could say that a set is a *collection*, a *union*, an *ensemble*, a *family*, a *system*, a *class*, etc. But this would not be a mathematical definition, but rather a misuse of the multitude of words available in the English language.

In order to define a concept we have to indicate first of all that it is a special case of a more general concept. This is impossible for the concept of set, since this concept is already as broad as possible and is thus not a special case of any other concept.

So, instead of giving a definition of the concept of set, we shall simply illustrate its nature by means of examples.

It is frequently necessary to speak of various objects which share some general property. For example, we might

16

talk about the set of chairs in a room, about the set of all atoms in Jupiter, about the set of all cells in the human body, about the set of all potatoes in a particular sack, about the set of all fish in the ocean, about the set of all squares in the plane, about the set of all points on a given circle, etc.

The objects which compose the given set are called its *elements*. In order to indicate that a given set A consists of elements x we usually write

$$A = \{x\} \tag{2.1}$$

Here the braces mean that the elements x are united into a new whole—the set A. We represent the statement that element x belongs to set A with the aid of the symbol as follows: $x \in A$. If the element x does not belong to set A, then we write $x \notin A$. For instance, if A denotes the set of all even natural numbers, then $6 \in A$, while $3 \notin A$.

Thus, when we speak of a set, we unite many objects into a new entity; namely, into the set which consists of these elements. The founder of the theory of sets, Georg Cantor, stressed this in the following words:

The set is a multitude conceived of by us as a one.

In order to gain insight into the notion of set, the academician N. N. Luzin proposed the following way of representing it. Imagine a transparent, impenetrable shell, something like a tightly closed, transparent sack. We suppose that all the elements of a given set A are contained within this shell, and that no other objects are present within the shell except these. This same transparent shell enclosing all the elements (and nothing besides them) is a rather good representation of the act of uniting all the elements x, the result of which is to construct the set A.

If the set contains a finite number of elements, we call the set *finite*, and if the set contains infinitely many elements, we call the set *infinite*. For example, the set of trees in the forest is finite, while the set of points on a circle is infinite.

How We Specify a Set

Of course, there are various ways of specifying a set. One way is to give a complete list of the elements composing a set. For instance, the set of pupils in a given class is determined by the list in the class register, the set of all countries on the globe is listed in any atlas, the set of all bones in the human skeleton is listed in textbooks of anatomy.

But we can only apply this method to finite sets, and certainly not even to all of them. As an example, take the set of fishes in the sea; it is finite, but it is hardly possible to give a list of all of them. We could not even begin

Fig. 3.   The great census of the fishes.

to define an infinite set with the aid of a list; for example, try to make a list of all the natural numbers—it is clear that the construction of this list could never be completed.

In those cases in which the set cannot be specified by means of a list, we determine it by making use of some characteristic property that is possessed by all elements of the set, but which no other objects possess. We might, for example, speak of the set of all natural numbers. It is then clear that the number 73 belongs to this set, while the

FIG. 4. The crocodile does not belong to the set of natural numbers.

number 3/4 or a crocodile does not belong. In exactly the same way neither $\sqrt{2}$ nor the planet Saturn belongs to the set of all rational numbers, while 7/15 does belong to this set.

In practice, let us note, the determination of sets by means of characterizing criteria runs into difficulty because of the ambiguity of our language. The task of separating the objects belonging to a set from those that do not is often made difficult by the large number of objects of intermediate type. Suppose, for example, that we are talking about the set of all trees on our globe. First of all, we must decide whether we mean all the trees which existed or will exist, or whether we mean the trees which existed during the course of a fixed interval of time (perhaps from the 1st of May to the 1st of September 1967). But how about the trees that were cut down during this period of time? Moreover, there exists a whole series of intermediate forms separating trees from other types of plants, so that we have to decide which of these are to belong to the set and which are not.

Similarly, when we discuss the set of all lines of poetry published in the year 1967, we are confronted with the existence of numerous forms of writing intermediate between poetry and prose (rhythmical prose, blank verse, etc). It is not too difficult to define the set of people who enjoy the right of free travel on the railroads of the Soviet Union. In particular, in this set we have all children less than 5 years old. But it might happen that one of our youthful passengers has his fifth birthday in the course of the trip, so that it becomes unclear whether or not he belongs to the set (let us say that one punctilious father uses a stop watch to determine exactly the remaining portion of the journey for which he is to pay, starting from the moment his son becomes five years old).

Subtle points like this crop up even in simpler cases. Suppose, for example, that the set A consists of all the letters of the first line of the famous story *Eugene Onegin*. This definition can be understood in two ways. On the one hand, we could be talking about the set composed of all the letters in this line; then each letter occurs in the set as many times as it occurs in the line (in order to distinguish the letters from one another we can use numerical indices);

$$М_1, О_1, Й_1, Д_1, Я_1, Д_2, Я_2, С_1, А_1, М_2,$$

$$Ы_1, Х_1, Ч_1, Е_1, С_2, Т_1, Н_1, Ы_2, Х_2, П_1,$$

$$Р_1, А_2, В_1, И_1, Л_1 \qquad (2.2)$$

But we could also suppose that we were talking about the set of distinct letters of the Russian alphabet which occurred in this line. In this case we would drop any repetitions of a letter, so that the set would consist of the following letters:

$$М, О, Й, Д, Я, С, А, Ы, Х, Ч, Е, Т, Н, П, Р, В, И, Л \quad (2.3)$$

It is clear that (2.2) and (2.3) are two distinct sets.

To Shave or Not to Shave?

Not all the difficulties connected with the determination of a set relate to inadequacies of language. Sometimes the cause lies deeper. As a rule, the set itself is not one of its elements (for example, the set of all natural numbers is not a natural number, the set of all triangles is not a triangle, etc). In general, however, the nature of the elements of a set is quite arbitrary, and no one can prohibit us from discussing sets which contain themselves as elements. Since such sets are discussed only rarely, we shall call them *exceptional* sets, while the remaining sets shall be called *ordinary* sets.

We can now describe the set *A* consisting of *all* ordinary sets. At first glance, there does not appear to be anything wrong with this definition; it is not obvious why the phrase "set of all ordinary sets" is any more wrong than the phrase "set of all triangles." But here we run into a serious logical contradiction, indeed. Let us try to make clear why this same set *A* is both ordinary and exceptional. If it is ordinary, then it occurs as one of its own elements (after all, we have collected together all ordinary sets). But then by definition it must be exceptional. If the set *A* is exceptional, then, by definition of exceptional set, it must be one of its own elements, but all the elements of A are ordinary sets; so we didn't take an exceptional set after all.

We have obtained an insoluble logical contradiction: the set A can neither be ordinary nor exceptional. Moreover, such logical contradictions arise in even simpler cases. A

FIG. 5. To shave or not to shave?

soldier was ordered to shave those soldiers and only those soldiers of his platoon who did not shave themselves. The question arose of whether he should shave himself. If he shaved himself, then he would be among the group of soldiers who shaved themselves, but he doesn't have the right to shave those soldiers. If he doesn't shave himself, then he belongs to the class of soldiers who do not shave themselves, but then according to the order he has been given he must shave himself.

There are other well-known examples of sets which at first glance appear to be well defined, but turn out on closer inspection to be very poorly defined, and we would be better off saying that these sets are not defined at all. For example, let A be the set of real numbers which can be defined with the aid of at most two hundred English words (here we include the words "zero," "one," "two," etc).

Since the set of all English words is finite (for simplicity we may assume that we only choose words found in Webster's dictionary and their grammatical derivatives), the set of all such real numbers is finite. But this means that the set can be enumerated. Let us suppose that this enumeration has already been carried out, and let us define the number N in the following way. This number has the form

$$N = 0, n_1 n_2 n_3 \ldots n_k \ldots \qquad (2.4)$$

Here we look at the kth digit occurring in the kth number in our list of the set A and agree to set $n_k = 1$, if this digit is distinct from 1. If the kth digit of the kth number is 1, then we put $n_k = 2$.

Thus, N is not equal to the kth number of set A, since it differs from it at the kth place. Since k was arbitrary, it follows that N cannot equal any number of set A and so does not belong to this set. However, N has to belong to the set A, because we used less than two hundred words in its definition.

This paradox is closely related to the following one:

What is the smallest integer that cannot be defined by means of a sentence having less than two hundred English words?

Such a number exists since the number of words in the English language is finite; so that there must be a number that cannot be defined by means of a sentence having less than two hundred words. And, of course, among these numbers there would have to be a smallest.

On the other hand, this number cannot exist, since its definition involves a contradiction. Indeed, this number is defined by the sentence written above in italics, which we see contains less than two hundred words; while according to its definition this number cannot be determined by such a sentence.

Many examples occur in the theory of sets in which the definition of the set is self-contradictory. The study of the question of the conditions under which this takes place leads to deep questions of logic. Consideration of these questions has completely changed the face of the subject. Many of these studies were subsequently used in constructing the theory of electronic computers, in the theory of automata, etc. Since these investigations belong rather to the subject of mathematical logic, we shall not touch on them here.

We shall only be concerned with sets which are well defined and defined in such a way that there is no question at this point (such as the set of all natural numbers, the set of all squares in the plane and so on).

The Empty Set

The very name "set" leads us to think that any set must contain many elements (at least two). But this is not the case. In mathematics it is sometimes necessary to examine sets having only one element and sometimes even a set having no elements at all. This set is called the *empty set* and is denoted by the symbol $\varnothing$.

Why should we be interested in an empty set?

First of all, let us take note of the fact that when a set is determined by means of some characteristic property, it is not always known in advance whether there are any elements with this property. For instance, let the set A consist of all quadrilaterals such that

(a) all of their angles are right angles,
(b) the diagonals have different lengths.

If someone does not know geometry, he will not see anything contradictory in these requirements. However, it follows from the theorem on the equality of the diagonals of a rectangle that the set of all such quadrilaterals is empty. The same is true of the set of all triangles the sum of whose angles is different from 180°. The set of quadratic polynomials having more than two roots is likewise empty. More generally, many mathematical statements can be formulated so as to become statements about the emptiness of a certain set (try to formulate the theorem of Pythagoras in this way).

There are also sets nonmathematical in nature that are empty: the set of all people whose age is more than 300 years, the set of all carp who live on land, the set of all planets of the solar system rotating about the star Sirius.

There are also some sets about which we do not know whether they are empty or not. For example, it is unknown at present whether the set of all natural numbers n such that $n > 2$ and n satisfies the equation

$$x^n + y^n = z^n \tag{2.5}$$

is empty or not (this is the famous problem of Fermat). It is also not known whether the set of digits occurring at most a finite number of times in the decimal expansion of π is empty or not (although the decimal expansion of π has been carried out to several thousands of digits, it is still unknown whether all digits occur in its decimal expansion an infinite number of times or whether some digit only occurs in it a finite number of times).

We also don't know if the set of all living plesiosaurs on earth is empty—if the Loch Ness monster really turns out to be a plesiosaur, then this set is not empty.

The Theory of Sets and Elementary Mathematics

A set can be composed of quite varied elements: fish, houses, squares, numbers, points, etc. Indeed, this explains the extraordinary breadth of the theory of sets and its applicability to the most varied branches of knowledge (mathematics, mechanics, physics, biology, linguistics, etc.). For mathematics, of course, the sets composed of "mathematical objects" play an especially important role; among these mathematical objects are geometric figures, algebraic equations, functions, etc. Some of these sets are involved in elementary mathematics, but the word "set" is usually lacking there (this is explained simply if we recall that the most "modern" part of elementary mathematics came into being at the end of the 17th century, while the theory of sets is a child of the 19th century).

Indeed, in elementary mathematics we encounter sets at every turn. Sets of numbers, i.e., sets composed of numbers, are met with especially frequently. As examples of such sets we can take:

(a)   the set of all natural numbers,
(b)   the set of all integers (positive, negative, and zero),
(c)   the set of all rational numbers,
(d)   the set of all real numbers,
(e)   the set of all complex numbers.

Two kinds of sets turn up in geometry. First of all, in geometry we ordinarily talk about the properties of some set of geometric figures. For example, the theorem stating that the diagonals of a parallelogram bisect each other relates to the set of all parallelograms. Secondly, the geometric figures are themselves sets composed of the points occurring within them. We can therefore speak of the set of all points contained within a given circle, of the set of all points within a given cone, etc.

In algebra we meet such sets as the set of all polynomials in two variables, the set of all quadratic equations, the set of all roots of a given equation, etc. In other words, almost every part of elementary mathematics is connected with the theory of sets in some way or other.

Subsets

The concept of set turns out to be very useful in mathematics. This is due to the fact that the elements of a set can be of the most varied nature. The same statement in terms of sets can be interpreted as a statement concerning points of a geometric figure, as a statement concerning natural numbers, as a statement concerning animals or plants, and as a statement concerning atoms and molecules. The concepts and theorems of the theory of sets have wide generality. We shall now discuss some of them. We need first to become acquainted with the notion of *subset*. This notion comes up each time we have to consider a set not only in itself but as a part of another, larger set. In fact, we say that set B is a subset of set A, if each element x in B is also an element of A. Here we write $B \subset A$.

For example, if we pick some high school, the set of sophomores is a subset of the set of all students in the school.

In turn, the set of students in this school is a subset of the set of all students.

In geometry too, we frequently have to deal with subsets of some set of geometric figures. Consider, for example, the following sets:

(a) Set A consists of all quadrilaterals;
(b) set B consists of all trapezoids;
(c) set C consists of all parallelograms;
(d) set D consists of all rectangles;
(e) set E consists of all squares.

In this list each figure is a special case of the figure of the preceding type (the trapezoid is a special type of quadrilateral, the parallelogram is a special type of trapezoid, etc). But this means that each set is a subset of its predecessor:

$$A \supset B \supset C \supset D \supset E \qquad (2.6)$$

Similarly, each set in the following list is a subset of its predecessor.

(a) The set of all complex numbers,
(b) the set of all real numbers,
(c) the set of all rational numbers,
(d) the set of all integers,
(e) the set of all natural numbers.

In many cases, in order to single out a subset from a given set it is sufficient to specialize the characterizing property of the set in some way or to give some supplementary condition. For example, the subset of natural numbers can be obtained from the set of integers by adding on the condition $n > 0$.

The Universal Set

Very rarely we might happen to be carrying out a discussion in which both the set of all complex numbers and the set of all whales in the ocean occurred (of course, we cannot exclude the possibility that the theory of functions of a complex variable might be applicable to the study of the motion of whales in water). More commonly, we find that all the sets involved in a discussion are subsets of some fixed set *I*. In this case we call the set *I* the *universal set*.

For example, in arithmetic the universal set is the set of all nonnegative rational numbers, in algebra it is the set of complex numbers and algebraic functions, in mathematical analysis it is the set of real functions of a real variable, and in geometry it is the set of all points in Euclidean space. Any geometric figure is, of course, a subset of the set of all points of Euclidean space.

The Intersection of Sets

In applications of mathematics we often have to deal with those elements of a collection of sets which occur in each set of the collection. These elements form a new set called the *intersection* of the given sets or their (*set*) *product*. And this operation of forming a new set is called *taking the intersection* or *multiplying* the sets in question. Thus, *taking the intersection of some sets A, B, C,... results in a new set containing just those elements which occur in each of the sets A, B, C,... .*

The name "intersection" derives from the fact that when we take the intersection of the sets of points in two geometric figures, we obtain the intersection of the two figures in the ordinary sense of the word. In Fig. 6 we show a line intersecting a circle in the chord AB. The set of points on this segment is the intersection of the set of points of the line with the set of points of the circle.

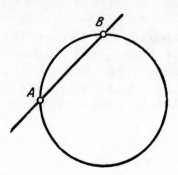

FIG. 6.   A line intersecting a circle in the chord AB.

But the concept of intersection is not only applicable to geometric figures. For example, suppose that the students of a given school participate in four kinds of sport: football, swimming, chess, and boxing. The intersection of the sets of participants in each sport will consist of those all-round athletes who play football, swim, box, and know the chess openings.

We sometimes have to take the intersection of sets of geometric figures or numbers. For instance, the set of all squares is the intersection of the set of all rectangles with the set of all rhombuses. The set of all right triangles is the intersection of all triangles with the set of all polygons containing right angles. The intersection of the set of all natural numbers divisible by 2 with the set of all natural numbers divisible by 3 is the set of all natural numbers divisible by 6.

The intersection of two sets A and B is usually denoted by either AB or $A \cap B$. The operation of taking the intersection possesses properties reminiscent of those possessed by the operation of multiplying numbers. Namely, it satisfies the commutative and associative laws

$$AB = BA \qquad (2.7)$$

and

$$A(BC) = (AB)C \qquad (2.8)$$

The empty set plays a role in the intersection (multiplication) of sets similar to the role played by zero in multiplication of numbers. In fact, for any set A we have the equality

$$AO = O \qquad (2.9)$$

analogous to the equality $a \cdot 0 = 0$.

The universal set plays a role analogous to that of unity: for any subset A of I we have the equality

$$AI = A \qquad (2.10)$$

analogous to the equality $a \cdot 1 = a$.

However, there are properties of set multiplication which are not analogous to properties of numerical multiplication. For example, if B is a subset of A, $B \subset A$, then we have the equality $BA = B$. For in this case all the elements of B (and just those elements) are simultaneously in both A and B.

In particular, for any set A we have the equality

$$AA = A \qquad (2.11)$$

Union of Sets

We now study the union of sets, which amounts to forming a new whole out of several sets. The *union* (or sum) of sets $A, B, \ldots$ is a new set consisting of just those elements that occur in at least one of the sets in question. The union of two sets A and B is usually denoted by $A + B$ or $A \cup B$.

We have to bear in mind that some of the elements may occur in more than one of the sets in question. In spite of this, they still occur only once in the union. Thus, if the sets involved are finite, it may turn out that the number of elements in the union is less than the sum of the numbers of elements in the individual sets. For example, let the first set be the set of all letters of the Russian alphabet occurring in the first line of "Eugene Onegin," and the second consist of the letters occurring in the second line of this poem. We have already written down the first set. It consists of the **18** letters

$$М, О, Й, Д, Я, С, А, Ы, Х, Ч, Е, Т, Н, П, Р, В, И, Л \quad (2.3)$$

The second set consists of the **13** letters:

$$К, О, Г, Д, А, Н, Е, В, Ш, У, Т, З, М \quad (2.12)$$

The union of these two sets is the following collection of **23** letters:

$$М, О, Й, Д, Я, С, А, Ы, Х, Ч, Е, Т, Н, П, Р,$$
$$В, И, Л, К, Г, Ш, У, З \quad (2.13)$$

The letters О, Д, А, Н, Е, В, Т, М, occurring in the intersection of these two sets occur only once in the union, so that we obtain only **23** letters rather than $18 + 13 = 31$ letters.

Here is yet another example in which the individual sets have elements in common. The set of all students in the class is the union of the following three sets:

(a) the set of passing students,
(b) the set of girls in the class,
(c) the set of boys who are not passing.

It is clear that every student of the class belongs to at least one of these three sets. However, these sets have common elements: the girls who are passing are in both the first and the second sets.

Sometimes the union is taken over an infinite collection of sets. For example, let A_n denote the set of all positive fractions with denominator n:

$$A_1 = \left\{\frac{m}{1}\right\}, \quad A_2 = \left\{\frac{m}{2}\right\}, \quad \ldots, \quad A_n = \left\{\frac{m}{n}\right\}, \quad \ldots \quad (2.14)$$

The union of all the sets $A_1, A_2, \ldots, A_n, \ldots$ is the set of all positive fractions, i.e., all the fractions of the type m/n, where m and n are natural numbers.

Let A_3 denote the set of all right triangles, let A_4 denote the set of right quadrilaterals, let A_5 denote the set of right five sided figures, etc. Then the union of all these sets is the set A of all right polygons.

Set unions also occur in algebra. If A is the set of roots of the equation

$$f(x) = 0 \qquad (2.15)$$

and B is the set of roots of the equation

$$\varphi(x) = 0 \qquad (2.16)$$

then the set of roots of the equation

$$f(x)\varphi(x) = 0 \qquad (2.17)$$

is $A + B$ (here we do not take the multiplicity of a root into account).

The operation of taking the union of sets has many properties analogous to those of the addition of numbers. Thus, we have the commutative and associative laws:

$$A + B = B + A \qquad (2.18)$$

and

$$A + (B + C) = (A + B) + C \qquad (2.19)$$

The empty set again plays the role of zero in the union of sets: no matter what set A is chosen, we always have the equality

$$A + O = A \qquad (2.20)$$

But the role of the universal set is no longer the role of unity in the addition of numbers. For any set A we have

$$A + I = I \qquad (2.21)$$

In general, if B is a subset of A, then $B + A = A$. In particular, for any set A we have $A + A = A$.

The operations of addition and multiplication of sets obey the distributive law

$$A(B + C) = AB + AC \qquad (2.22)$$

In order to show that this law is obeyed we have to show that each element on the left-hand side of the equality is present on the right-hand side, and conversely.

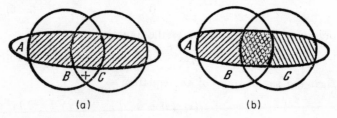

(a)   (b)

FIG. 7a, b.   Illustration of equality (2.22).

It is not difficult to carry out a rigorous proof of this law, but the details are somewhat tedious. For this reason we shall simply present two figures which illustrate equality (2.22). The shaded region in Fig. 7a is the intersection of set A with the set $B + C$; in Fig. 7b we show the intersection of A with B and A with C. It is quite obvious from these pictures that equality (2.22) holds. Moreover, for sets there is another "distributive law" which does not hold for numbers. It is expressed in the formula

$$A + BC = (A + B)(A + C) \qquad (2.23)$$

It can be proved simply by expanding the right-hand side according to formula (2.22) and taking note of the fact that AB and AC are both subsets of A; thus, $AC \subset A$ and $AB \subset A$. In addition, $AA = A$, so that

$$AA + AC + BA + BC = A + BC \qquad (2.24)$$

Partitioning of Sets

Considered in general, the summands occurring in a union of sets may have elements in common. However, we sometimes encounter a set which is the union of its own subsets, no two of which have elements in common (or, as we would usually say, no two intersect). In this case we say that set A has a *decomposition into disjoint subsets*.

Decompositions into subsets frequently arise in the classification of objects. For example, when a catalog of the books in a library is being compiled, they are first divided into works of fiction, books of political and social science, books on the natural sciences, etc. After this, each of the subsets obtained is further subdivided into smaller subsets: works of fiction are divided into prose and poetry, books on the social and political sciences are divided into books on philosophy, political economy, etc., books on the natural sciences are divided into books on mathematics, physics, etc. This subdivision makes it convenient to find any desired book.

Of course, the same set can be decomposed into disjoint subsets in different ways. When, in that same library, they compile the alphabetic index, they first divide the books into the subset of books whose authors' names begin with A, the subset of books whose authors' names begin with B, etc. After this each of the subsets is again subdivided in correspondence with the second letter of an authors' name, etc.

The concept of *equivalence* of elements is frequently used in the decomposition of sets. We first have to define what is meant by the phrase "element x is equivalent to element y," and we can then unite all equivalent elements in one subset. However, not just any notion of equivalence will do for a decomposition. For example, we could say that two people are equivalent if they know one another. But it can happen that person X knows person Y, that person Y knows person Z, while person X and person Z are not acquainted. Then we have to put people X and Y in the same subset (they know one another), after that Z must also be included (he knows Y), so we find that in our subset we have people that are not acquainted: X and Z. In order to avoid this undesirable situation it is necessary that the notion of equivalence satisfy the following three conditions:

(a) each element is equivalent to itself;

(b) if element x is equivalent to element y, then element y is equivalent to element x;

(c) if element x is equivalent to element y and element y is equivalent to element z, then element x is equivalent to element z.

It can be proved that the fulfillment of these three conditions is necessary and sufficient for a decomposition of A into subsets of mutually equivalent elements to exist (moreover, distinct subsets have no elements in common).

For example, we might say that two integers x and y are equivalent if their difference is an even integer. It is easy to verify that this definition of equivalence satisfies all three conditions (a)–(c). By gathering all mutually equivalent integers into a subset we effect a partition of the set of all integers into two subsets: the set of even integers and the set of odd integers.

Subtraction of Sets

When there is a notion of sum, a notion of difference can usually be found. Sets are not an exception to this rule. The difference of sets A and B will be a new set $A - B$, in which there occur all those elements of set A which do not belong to set B. Here we need make no requirement about B being a subset of A. If B is not a subset of A, then the subtraction of B from A reduces to the removal from A of the common part of A and B:

$$A - B = A - AB \qquad (2.25)$$

For example, if A is the set of points contained in the first circle appearing in Fig. 8 and B is the set of points

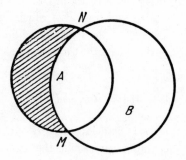

Fig. 8.

contained in the second circle, then their difference is the
set of points contained in the shaded crescent-shaped figure
(minus the arc MN). If A is the set of all students of a given
class in some school and B is the set of all girls attending
this school, then $A - B$ is the set of all boys who are students
in the class in question.

In case B is a subset of A, we say that $A - B$ is the
complement of set B relative to A and denote it by B'_A
(of course, the same set B will have different complements
relative to different sets A containing it). For example,
the complement of the set of even numbers relative to the
set of all integers is the set of all odd numbers. The complement of the set of all squares in the set of all rectangles is
the set of all rectangles with unequal adjacent sides. On the
other hand, the complement of this same set of squares in the
set of all rhombuses is the set of rhombuses with unequal
diagonals.

If all the sets under consideration are subsets of a universal set I, then by the complement of the set B we usually
understand its complement relative to I. In this case we
write B' instead of B'_I.

Due to the fact that elements occurring in several of the
summands only occur once in the union of the summands,
and since it is possible to subtract a set which is not contained
in the minuend, several of the formulas of arithmetic cease
to hold for subtraction of sets. It may happen, for instance,
that

$$(A + B) - C \neq A + (B - C) \tag{2.26}$$

Indeed, if all three sets coincide, $A = B = C$, then the left
hand side is the empty set, while the right-hand side is
equal to A.

The Algebra of Sets

We have become acquainted with operations on sets as well as with some properties of these operations. In addition to these properties we might have discussed a whole series of others. We shall now present a list of all the general properties of the set-theoretical operations introduced (in this list O will denote the empty set, I will denote the universal set, A' will denote the complement of set A with respect to the universal set):

[1] $A \subset A$.

[2]   If $A \subset B$ and $B \subset A$, then $A = B$.

[3]   If $A \subset B$ and $B \subset C$, then $A \subset C$.

[4] $O \subset A$.

[5] $A \subset I$.

[6] $A + B = B + A$.

[7] $AB = BA$.

[8] $A + (B + C) = (A + B) + C$.

[9] $A(BC) = (AB)C$.

[10] $A + A = A$.

[11] $AA = A$.

[12] $A(B + C) = AB + AC$.

[13] $A + BC = (A + B)(A + C)$.

[14] $A + O = A$.

[15] $AI = A$.

[16] $A + I = I$.

[17] $AO = O$.

[18] The relation $A \subset B$ is equivalent to either of the relations $A + B = B$, $AB = A$.

[19] $A + A' = I$.

[20] $AA' = O$.

[21] $O' = I$.

[22] $I' = O$.

[23] $(A')' = A$.

[24] The relation $A \subset B$ is equivalent to the relation $B' \subset A'$.

[25] $(A + B)' = A'B'$.
[26] $(AB)' = A' + B'$.

Using properties [1–26], we can carry out operations on sets in exactly the same way as we carry out operations on numbers in ordinary algebra. In fact, certain formulas have an even simpler form than in ordinary algebra. For example, the binomial formula reduces to the following simple equality:

$$(A + B)^n = A + B \qquad (2.27)$$

as may be readily checked by use of property [11].

We shall not prove properties [1–26]; they can be checked by use of pictures (Venn diagrams) just as we checked property [12]. The proof of properties [25] and [26] is a little more complicated than that of the others.

Of course, it is not an easy task to commit properties [1–26] to memory. But this is not at all necessary; indeed, it is enough to become acquainted with the two fundamental operations: addition of sets and the taking of complements. The latter two operations must satisfy the following three relations:

$$A + B = B + A \qquad (2.28)$$

$$(A + B) + C = A + (B + C) \qquad (2.29)$$

$$(A' + B')' + (A' + B)' = A \qquad (2.30)$$

We can now define the operation of multiplication AB and the containment relation $A \subset B$ by means of the formulas

$$AB = (A' + B')' \qquad \text{(by definition)} \qquad (2.31)$$

$$A \subset B \quad \text{means} \quad A + B = B \qquad (2.32)$$

Then all the properties [1–26] will follow from formulas (2.28)–(2.32).

We point out the following remarkable "duality relation."
If in each of the properties [1–26] we interchange the symbols

$$\subset \quad \text{and} \quad \supset$$

$$O \quad \text{and} \quad I$$

$$+ \quad \text{and} \quad \cdot$$

then in each case the result of the interchange is again one
of the above properties. For example, if we apply this
procedure to property [6], property [7] results; if we apply
it to property [12], property [13] results, etc.

It follows from this that whenever a theorem can be
proved by use of properties [1–26], then its corresponding
"dual theorem," obtained by interchanging the indicated
symbols, is also true.

Boolean Algebras

In addition to sets, we encounter other objects in mathematics for which operations of addition and multiplication
possessing properties [1–26] are defined. Such collections
of objects were first studied in 1847 by the English mathematician Boole. Such systems are therefore called *Boolean
algebras*.

An interesting example of a Boolean algebra is formed
by the set of all divisors of the number 30: $M = \{1, 2, 3, 5,
6, 10, 15, 30\}$. Here the operation of "addition" is to be
the formation of the least common multiple, while that of
"multiplication" is to be the formation of the greatest
common divisor. For example, $2 \oplus 5 = 10$, $6 \odot 15 = 3$
(we have enclosed the symbols of addition and multiplication in circles in order to distinguish them from the usual
addition and multiplication of numbers). The relation

$a \subset b$ means that a is a divisor of the number b. The role of the element O is played by the number 1, while the number 30 plays the role of the element I. As the complement of the divisor a we must take the number $a' = 30/a$. For example, $10' = 3$.

Of course, it is not necessary to verify that all of the properties [1–26] hold; as we mentioned above, it is sufficient to verify that properties (2.28)–(2.32) are satisfied for this system.

3

The Cardinality of Sets

Equality between Sets

Up till now we have been concerned with properties of sets which held generally for both finite and infinite sets. Here we shall be interested in properties characteristic of infinite sets alone. We have already seen in the story of Ion the Quiet that these properties are quite different from those of finite sets—things impossible for finite sets turn out to be possible for infinite sets.

The first question which we shall now discuss is the problem of deciding when two infinite sets are equal to one another. For finite sets of the most varied types we can always say which of them contains the larger number of elements. This problem is much more complicated for infinite sets. For example, which is the larger set, that of the natural numbers or that of the rational numbers, that of the rational numbers or that of the real numbers? Are there more points on the entire line than there are on a segment, more points in a square than on a line?

It appears quite simple at first glance to answer these questions. After all, the set of natural numbers is only a part of the set of rational numbers and the segment is only a part of the line. Isn't it obvious, therefore, that there are fewer natural numbers than there are rational numbers and that there are fewer points on a segment than in a square? It turns out not to be so obvious. It does not follow at all that when we go from finite to infinite sets, the laws derived from the study of the former remain valid; for example, a law such as "the part is less than the whole."

Above all, an attempt to base equality for infinite sets on the criterion that one is a part of the other is doomed to failure in advance. For example, where are there more points, in a square or on the whole of an infinite line? After all, the square cannot be contained in a line and, without breaking it, it is impossible to put a line inside a square. Of course, it is possible to break the line up into segments of length equal to the side of the square, and after that place each segment inside the square in such a way that no two intersect. But how do we know that we can find a way to break up the square so that the parts can be strung out along the line without overlapping? And how many infinite sets there are which are not parts of one another! The set of squares in the plane and the set of circles in the same plane do not have even a single element in common. How can we compare them? How can we find out if there are more atoms of nitrogen or of oxygen in the universe?

We have now posed the problem. First we investigate under what conditions it can be said that one set contains just as many elements as another. In other words, we study the conditions under which two infinite sets have "the same measure" of elements.

On the Dance Floor

The problem of comparison is easily solved for finite sets. In order to find out if the number of elements is the same for two sets, we have only to count them. If we get the same numbers, this means that both sets have the same size. But such a procedure is not suitable for infinite sets; for, having begun to count the elements of an infinite set, we run the risk of devoting our entire lives to this job and still not completing the enterprise we have undertaken.

And the method of counting is not always convenient even for finite sets. For instance, let us go to a dance hall. How can we tell if the numbers of boys and girls here are the same? Of course, we could ask the boys to go off to one side and the girls to the other, and undertake to count both groups. But, in the first place, this would give us superfluous information; we are not interested in how many boys and girls are here, but only in whether the numbers are the same. And then, the young people on the dance floor did not get together to stand around and wait for the end of the count, but to dance.

Well, what then? Let us satisfy their wish and ask the orchestra to play a dance that everybody knows how to do. Then the boys will ask the girls to dance and ... our problem will be solved. After all, if it turns out that all the boys and girls are dancing, i.e., if all the young people are paired off, then it is obvious that there are just as many boys as girls on the dance floor.

We could find out by an identical procedure whether the number of spectators in a theater is equal to the number of seats. If during the performance all the places are taken, no spectator is standing in the aisles and one spectator is sitting in each seat, then we can be sure that there are just as many spectators as seats.

When people are running down the street in rainy weather, the number of people is the same as the number of raincoats; for each person wears only one raincoat and no one would risk running along the street without a raincoat.

For Every Flow There Is an Ebb

We have seen how it is possible to determine that two finite sets have equally many elements without having recourse to counting. We can also apply this method to infinite sets. But here we can no longer get an orchestra to do the job; we ourselves have to distribute the elements of the two sets to be compared into "couples."

Then suppose we are given two sets A and B. We shall say that we have established a *one-to-one correspondence* between them, if the elements of these sets have been joined in pairs (a, b) such that:

(1) element a belongs to set A, and element b belongs to set B;

(2) every element of the two sets occurs in one and only one pair.

For instance, if set A consists of the boys on the dance floor and set B consists of the girls found there, then pair (a, b) is composed of the boy and girl dancing together. If set A consists of the spectators and set B consists of the seats in the theater, then pair (a, b) is composed of the spectator and the seat in which he sits. Finally, if A is the set of people on the street and B is the set of their raincoats, then pair (a, b) is composed of the person and his raincoat.

Naturally, not every correspondence between sets is one-to-one. If set A consists of all the trees in the world and set B consists of all the fruit growing on these trees, then we can set up the following correspondence between these sets: to each fruit we make correspond the tree on which it grows. But this is not a one-to-one correspondence: many pieces of fruit grow on some trees, while other trees do not even bear fruit. Thus, some elements *a* (trees) will appear in many pairs, while other elements *a* will not appear in any.

It means the same thing for two finite sets to say that there is a one-to-one correspondence between them, or to say that they have equally many elements. The fundamental turning point in the theory of sets came when Cantor decided to compare infinite sets in the same manner.

In other words, Cantor said that two (possibly infinite) sets *A* and *B* have equally many elements, if it is possible to set up a one-to-one correspondence between them.

Mathematicians do not usually say: "sets *A* and *B* have equally many elements"; they say: "*A* and *B* have the same *cardinality*" or they say: "sets *A* and *B* are *equivalent.*"

Because of this, the word *cardinality* means the same thing for infinite sets as the words "number of elements" do for finite sets.

The Czech savant B. Bolzano arrived at the notion of one-to-one correspondence independently of Cantor; but he gave up the further pursuit of the idea because of the difficulties into which it led him. As we shall soon see, we shall have to set aside many cherished habits of thought once we accept the principle of comparing infinite sets with the aid of the one-to-one correspondence.

Can a Part Be Equal to the Whole?

One dogma that we have to brush aside is the statement, established at the beginning of the development of mathematics: *a part is less than the whole*. This statement is indisputably true for finite sets, but it loses its force when

we try to apply it for infinite sets. Let us recall how the
director of the extraordinary hotel shifted the cosmic
zoologists to even-numbered rooms. He moved the inhabit-
ant of room n to room $2n$. In other words, he moved them
according to the following scheme:

$$
\begin{array}{ccccccc}
1 & 2 & 3 & \ldots & n & \ldots \\
\downarrow & \downarrow & \downarrow & & \downarrow & \\
2 & 4 & 6 & \ldots & 2n & \ldots
\end{array}
\tag{3.1}
$$

But this scheme sets up a one-to-one correspondence
between the set of natural numbers

$$
1, 2, 3, \ldots, n, \ldots
\tag{3.2}
$$

and a part of this set: the set of even numbers

$$
2, 4, 6, \ldots, 2n, \ldots
\tag{3.2a}
$$

But we agreed to assume that two sets contain equally
many elements if it is possible to set up a one-to-one correspondence between them. This means that the set of
natural numbers contains as many and only as many
elements as one of its subsets, the set of even numbers.

In exactly the same way we could set up a one-to-one
correspondence between the set of natural numbers and the
set of numbers of the form

$$
10, 100, 1000, 10\,000, \ldots
\tag{3.3}
$$

To do this we need only associate the natural number n
with the number 10^n:

$$
n \rightarrow 10^n
\tag{3.4}
$$

This establishes the desired one-to-one correspondence.
In the same way we can set up a one-to-one correspondence
between the set of all natural numbers and the set of all
squares of natural numbers:

$$
n \rightarrow n^2
\tag{3.5}
$$

the set of all cubes of natural numbers:

$$n \to n^3 \qquad (3.6)$$

and so on.

Generally speaking, we can set up a one-to-one correspondence between the set of all natural numbers and any of its infinite subsets. To do this we need only write down the numbers of this subset in a sequence.

Countable Sets

We call sets having equally many elements as the set of natural numbers *countable sets*. In other words, a set is called countable if it is infinite and its elements can be counted with the aid of the natural numbers. For example, the set of even numbers, the set of odd numbers, the set of primes, and, in general, any infinite subset of the natural numbers are countable sets.

We sometimes have to employ considerable ingenuity in order to show that this or that set is countable. Let us take as our example the set of all integers (both positive and negative):

$$\ldots, -n, \ldots, -3, -2, -1, 0, 1, 2, 3, \ldots, n, \ldots \quad (3.7)$$

If we try to number them beginning at some given place, we find that the numbering is incomplete; for all the numbers occurring before the given place have not been counted. In order not to leave out any numbers we have to write the set in two lines:

$$\begin{matrix} 0, & 1, & 2, & 3, & 4, & 5, & 6, \ldots \\ -1, & -2, & -3, & -4, & -5, & -6, & -7, \ldots \end{matrix} \qquad (3.8)$$

and number by columns. Here 0 is assigned the number 1, -1 is assigned the number 2, 1 the number 3, -2 the number 4, etc. In other words, zero and all the positive integers are numbered with odd numbers, while all the negative integers are numbered with even numbers. This resembles the way the hotel director placed the philatelists in a hotel already filled with cosmic zoologists.

But if it is easy to show that the set of integers is countable, it is more difficult to show that the same is true of the rational numbers. After all, the rationals are densely distributed: between any two rational numbers we can still find infinitely many rational numbers. So it is quite unclear how we should go about numbering them; it would seem that between any two numbers we would still have to number an infinite set, so that the process would never end. And it really is impossible to write down the rationals in a sequence in which each number is greater than its predecessor.

But if we do not concern ourselves about the magnitude of the numbers in our sequence, we can succeed in numbering them. Let us first write down all positive fractions with denominator 1, then all positive fractions with denominator 2, then with denominator 3, and so on. We get a tabulation like the following:

$$\frac{1}{1}, \quad \frac{2}{1}, \quad \frac{3}{1}, \quad \frac{4}{1}, \quad \frac{5}{1}, \ldots$$

$$\frac{1}{2}, \quad \frac{2}{2}, \quad \frac{3}{2}, \quad \frac{4}{2}, \quad \frac{5}{2}, \ldots$$

$$\frac{1}{3}, \quad \frac{2}{3}, \quad \frac{3}{3}, \quad \frac{4}{3}, \quad \frac{5}{3}, \ldots \tag{3.9}$$

$$\frac{1}{4}, \quad \frac{2}{4}, \quad \frac{3}{4}, \quad \frac{4}{4}, \quad \frac{5}{4}, \ldots$$

$$\frac{1}{5}, \quad \frac{2}{5}, \quad \frac{3}{5}, \quad \frac{4}{5}, \quad \frac{5}{5}, \ldots$$

$$\cdots\cdots\cdots\cdots\cdots\cdots\cdots\cdots\cdots$$

Clearly, every positive rational number will appear in this table, and more than once. For example, the number **3** occurs in the form of the fractions 3/1, 6/2, and 9/3.

Now we commence with the numbering. For this we recall the last exploit of the director of the extraordinary hotel, the one in which he found places for the guests of infinitely many such hotels. In doing this he numbered by squares. We shall proceed in the same manner, but with this complication: we shall leave out some of the fractions (for example, since 1/1 is assigned number 1, we drop the fractions 2/2, 3/3, etc, for they express the same number). We get the following enumeration of the positive rationals: 1, 2, 1/2, 3, 3/2, 2/3, 1/3, 4, 4/3, 3/4, 1/4, ...

Thus we can number all the positive rationals. It is now easy to explain how all the rational numbers (both positive and negative) can be numbered. We separate them into two tables, using even numbers to number one table and odd numbers for the other (remembering to reserve a number for zero).

In general, if we take the union of a countable set of countable sets, we again get a countable set. We could prove this by using this same technique of numbering by squares.

Algebraic Numbers

All the examples we have given up to this point are actually special cases of a general theorem. This comes about because in all of these examples the elements of the sets can be specified by means of a finite collection of natural numbers. For example, any integer n (except zero) can be written in the form

$$(-1)^k |n| \qquad\qquad (3.10)$$

where $|n|$ is the absolute value of the number, and k is 1, if $n < 0$, and 2, if $n > 0$. Thus the integer n is determined by means of a pair of natural numbers $(k, |n|)$. In the same way we can write any positive rational number in the form of an irreducible fraction m/n, or, what is the same thing, we can employ the pair of natural numbers (m, n).

The general theorem to which we referred reads as follows:

Theorem 3.1. *If every element in a set can be specified by means of a finite collection of natural numbers, then this set is finite or countable.*

The basic idea of the proof of Theorem 3.1 is quite similar to one of the methods employed by the director of the hotel in solving his most difficult problem; the details, however, are more complicated.

We start off by taking all the primes 2, 3, 5, 7, 11, 13, etc, writing them $p_1, p_2, \ldots, p_n, \ldots$. If the element x of A is specified by the collection of natural numbers $\{m_1, \ldots, m_n\}$, then we let it correspond to the natural number

$$N_x = p_1{}^{m_1} \ldots p_n{}^{m_n} \qquad (3.11)$$

It follows from the theorem asserting the uniqueness of the decomposition of natural numbers into products of primes that different elements of A correspond to different natural numbers. Thus, the mapping $x \to N_x$ sets up a one-to-one correspondence between the elements of set A and a subset of the natural numbers.

We shall prove later that any infinite subset of the natural numbers is countable, so that by combining this fact with the result of the previous paragraph we see that set A is either finite or countable.

With the help of this theorem we can prove, for example, that the set of all algebraic numbers is countable.

Algebraic numbers are roots of algebraic equations with integer coefficients $a_0, \ldots, a_n$:

$$a_0 x^n + a_1 x^{n-1} + \ldots + a_n = 0 \qquad (3.12)$$

For example, $\sqrt[4]{5}$ is an algebraic number, for it is a root of the equation

$$x^4 - 5 = 0 \qquad (3.13)$$

Numbers that are not algebraic are called *transcendental*.

Each equation of nth degree has exactly n roots. Thus, any algebraic number is determined by a collection of integers:

$$\{k, a_0, a_1, \ldots, a_n\} \qquad (3.14)$$

where $a_0, \ldots, a_n$ are the coefficients of Eq. (3.12) and k is the index of the root. The numbers $a_0, \ldots, a_n$ can assume any integral values, while k is a natural number between 1 and n. If we now apply Theorem 3.1, we see that the set of all algebraic integers is countable.*

Unequal Sets

We have already explained what we mean when we say: "two sets have equally many elements." Now we are going to explain what we mean when we say: "one set has more elements than another." For finite sets this too can be found out without resorting to counting. Recall our example involving the dance floor.

---

* The requirement that the numbers $a_0, \ldots, a_n$ be integers rather than natural numbers does not raise any problems, for the integers can be enumerated.

If, after the orchestra starts playing and the boys have invited the girls to dance, there are some boys leaning against the wall, then it is clear that there are more boys. On the other hand, if we see some girls sadly watching their friends dancing, it is clear that there are more girls.

Fig. 9.   An atom from each fish.

In these examples we proceeded as follows: we tried to establish a one-to-one correspondence between one set, the first, and part of another set, the second. If this worked out, then the second set had more elements than the first. By employing this method we could prove, for example, that there are fewer fish in the ocean than atoms on the Earth (although both these sets are finite, it is hardly possible to count them). We can do this by simply letting each fish correspond to one of the atoms constituting its body. This sets up a one-to-one correspondence between the set of all fish and part of the set of all atoms on Earth.

Fig. 10a.

Fig. 10b.
No partner for him.

Unfortunately, this simple procedure fails to hold good for infinite sets. Indeed, we recently saw that a set can have equally many elements as one of its parts. So we are in no position to conclude from the sole fact that A has as many elements as a part of set B, that set A has fewer elements than set B.

We shall be more modest in our demands and say that if we can set up a one-to-one correspondence between set A and part of set B, then set B has *no fewer elements than set A.* We could prove that this relation possesses all the fundamental properties of inequalities:

(1) Each set *A* has no fewer elements than itself.

(2) If set *A* has no fewer elements than set *B*, and *B* has no fewer elements than set *C*, then *A* has no fewer elements than *C*.

(3) If *A* has no fewer elements than *B*, and *B* has no fewer elements than *A*, then they have equally many elements (that is, we can set up a one-to-one correspondence between the elements of these sets).

It can happen that set *B* has no fewer elements than set *A*, but these sets are not equivalent. In other words, there could exist a one-to-one correspondence between set *A* and part B_1 of set *B* without there existing a one-to-one correspondence between *A* and all of set *B*. This is the case in which we shall say that *B* has more elements than *A*.

The Countable Set—The Smallest of the Infinite Sets

We already said that any infinite subset of the set of natural numbers is countable. This means that there can be no infinite set whose cardinality is less than the cardinality of a countable set. Let us now prove that any infinite set contains a countable subset. We can conclude from this that the cardinality of a countable set is not greater than the cardinality of any infinite set, i.e., that this cardinality is the smallest infinite cardinality.

We can select a countable subset from the infinite set *A* in the following way: Take any element x_1—we can do this because the set *A* is infinite, and so is certainly not empty. Clearly, we have not exhausted the elements of *A* with the selection of element x_1, so that we can proceed to select a second element x_2. After that, we choose a third element x_3, etc. We have thus extracted from set A a countable subset X of indexed elements:

$$X = \{x_1, x_2, \ldots, x_n, \ldots\} \tag{3.15}$$

By making a slight change in the argument we can arrange matters so that an infinite set will be left even after the extraction of the countable subset. All we have to do is put back into A all those elements from X that have even indices. After doing this, we have extracted a countable subset

$$Y = \{x_1, x_3, x_5, \ldots\} \tag{3.16}$$

and the remaining part of the set still contains an infinite subset of elements: $\{x_2, x_4, x_6, \ldots, x_{2n}, \ldots\}$ (and possibly other elements).

It is not difficult to prove the following theorems.

Theorem 3.2. *The cardinality of an infinite set is not changed when we adjoin a countable set to it.*

Theorem 3.3. *The cardinality of an uncountable set is not changed when we extract a countable subset from it.*

Theorems 3.2 and 3.3 again assert that the countable set is the smallest of the infinite sets.

Uncountable Sets

All the sets we have constructed so far have been countable. This naturally leads us to ask whether all infinite sets are countable. If so, the mathematician would have an easy life: all infinite sets would have equally many elements and no further analysis of infinity would be necessary. But the situation turns out to be more complicated than that; uncountable sets exist, and of more than one cardinality. We are already acquainted with one uncountable set—the set of all points on a straight line. But rather than speak of this set, we are going to discuss a set closely related to it, the set A of ways in which the rooms of the extraordinary hotel can be occupied.

Note that it is usually not easy to prove that a set is uncountable. After all, to prove that a set is countable means simply to invent a method of enumerating its elements. But to prove that a set is uncountable we have to prove that no such method exists. In other words, no matter what method we applied, some element of the set would fail to be counted. Cantor conceived of a very clever method for proving the uncountability of sets which is called the diagonal process (actually, we encountered it on p. 23). Cantor's method of proof is made clear by the following story about Ion the Quiet.

The Census That Never Took Place

Up to now I have talked about the successes of the director of the extraordinary hotel: about how he managed to find places for an infinite set of new guests in his already full hotel, and how he later was able to find places even for the guests from infinitely many such unusual hotels. But there was a time when even this wizard met failure.

An order came down from the commissioner of cosmic hotels to compile a list as quickly as possible of all the possible ways in which the rooms of the hotel could be occupied. The list was to be presented in the form of a table, each line of which was to reflect one of the various ways of occupying the hotel. The filled rooms were to be indicated by ones and the empty rooms by zeros. For example, the sequence

$$101010101010\ldots \qquad (3.17)$$

meant that all the odd rooms were filled and all the even rooms were empty. The sequence

$$11111111111\ldots \qquad (3.18)$$

meant that the entire hotel was filled, while the sequence

$$000000000000\ldots \qquad (3.19)$$

indicated a financial catastrophe—all the rooms were empty.

The director was overloaded with work and therefore conceived of a simple way out of the situation. He charged the man on duty on each floor to compose a list of the ways in which just the rooms in his charge could be occupied. No two ways on the list were to be the same. After a few days the lists were presented to the director and he combined them all into one list.

"Are you sure that this list is complete?" I asked the director. "Isn't there some other way of occupying the rooms?"

"I don't know" he replied. "There are infinitely many ways listed and I don't know how to test the list for completeness."

At this point an idea flashed into my head (by the way, I may be overestimating my talents, because not all traces of my discussions with Professor Tarantog on infinite sets had vanished from my mind).

"I can guarantee that the list is incomplete. I can select a way that is sure to be lacking."

"I agree that the list is probably incomplete. But you won't succeed in selecting a way that isn't listed; after all, there are already infinitely many listed."

We made a bet. I proposed to win it by nailing each sequence on the door of the room to which it corresponded (the reader will recall that there were just as many ways listed as rooms in the hotel). I then proceeded in a very simple fashion. Going up to the door of the first room, I saw that the corresponding sequence started with the digit 0. The digit 1 quickly appeared on my writing pad; this was the first digit of the sequence I wanted to construct.

When I went up to the door of the second room, I wasn't interested in the first digit of that sequence; after all, I already had the first digit of my sequence. So I directed my attention to the second digit. Seeing that this was 1, I wrote the digit 0 on my pad. Similarly, when I noticed that the third digit of the sequence nailed to the first room was also 1, I again wrote the digit 0 on my pad. In general, when I found that the nth digit of the nth sequence was 0, then I wrote the digit 1 in the nth place on my pad, but if the nth digit of the nth sequence was 1, then I wrote 0.

After I had gone past all the rooms of the hotel,* a sequence of zeros and ones had been written on my pad.

Going to the director's office, I said:

"Here, feast your eyes on the missing sequence."
"And how do you know that it's lacking?"
"It can't be the first because it has a different first digit. It can't be the second because it has a different second digit; in general, it can't be the nth because it has a different nth digit."

---

* Hm, how much time did he have to spend?

The bet was won, and I gained the privilege to stay at the hotel whenever I wanted at no charge.

But it at once became clear that no matter what countable set of sequences you took, there would always be a sequence that didn't appear in the list (you would always be able to hang them on the doors of the rooms). This means that the set of all ways of occupying the hotel is uncountable, and the task given the director was not one that could be carried out.

We decided to send a telegram describing the situation. I should point out that the telegraph in use at the extraordinary hotel was itself unusual: it could send telegrams composed of an infinite set (more precisely, a countable set) of dots and dashes. For example, the telegram might have the form

$$— \cdot — — \cdot — — — \cdot \quad \text{etc} \qquad (3.20)$$

I quickly grasped the fact that the set of all such telegrams was also uncountable; after all, you could just as well put zeros and ones in place of the dots and dashes, and then there would be no difference at all between the telegrams with a countable set of signs and the set of all ways of occupying the hotel.

After sending the telegram, I took leave of the director of the hotel and took off for galaxy RGC-8067, where I was to carry out an astrographical survey.

The Uncountability of the Continuum

Now it will not be difficult to prove that the set of all points on a line is uncountable. In place of it we can discuss the set of all real numbers, since to each point on the line there corresponds a real number, and conversely.

Any real number can be given an infinite decimal expansion of the form

$$a. \alpha_1 \alpha_2 \alpha_3 \ldots \alpha_n \ldots \tag{3.21}$$

Some even have two expansions, for example: 0.500000... and 0.49999999... both represent the same number. To simplify matters we shall employ the expansion with the zeros.

Suppose that by some scheme we had managed to enumerate all the real numbers. In order to show that this can't happen we need only show that some number has not been enumerated. Following in Ion the Quiet's footsteps, we proceed in the following manner.

We first write zero followed by a decimal point. We then take the first number in our enumeration and examine its first place after the decimal point (i.e., its tenths place). If it differs from 1, then we write a 1 after the decimal point in the number we are constructing; but if it is 1, we put a 2 after the decimal point. After that we choose the second number in our enumeration and examine its second place after the decimal point. Again, if this number is different from one, we put the number 1 in the hundredths place in our number; and if it is 1, then we use 2. We carry on in this way, each time looking at the nth place in the nth number of our enumeration. As a result of these operations we get some number, for example:

$$N = 0.1121211\ldots \tag{3.22}$$

It is clear that this number is not one of those enumerated: it differs from the first number in the first decimal place; it differs from the second number in the second decimal place; it differs from the nth number in the nth decimal place, etc. (compare p. 60).

In order to make it clearer to the reader how we determine our number different from all those enumerated, suppose that in the given enumeration the first five numbers have the following form:

$$4.27364\ldots$$

$$-1.31226\ldots$$

$$7.95471\ldots \tag{3.23}$$

$$0.62419\ldots$$

$$8.56280\ldots$$

Then the number not in the enumeration will begin with the following decimals:

$$0.12121\ldots \tag{3.24}$$

Naturally, this is not the only number that is not on the list (we could have replaced all the decimals except 2 by 2 and replaced 2 by 7, or chosen some other rule). But we only needed to establish the existence of one single number which does not appear in the enumeration in order to demonstrate that the supposed enumeration of all the real numbers could not exist.

The Existence of Transcendental Numbers

Numbers are called *transcendental numbers* if they are not the roots of any equation with integer coefficients of the form

$$a_0x^n + a_1x^{n-1} + \ldots + a_n = 0 \tag{3.25}$$

The numbers which are roots of such equations are called *algebraic numbers*.

During a long period in its history mathematics only dealt with algebraic numbers, such as $7/15$, $\sqrt[8]{10}$, $\sqrt{2} + \sqrt[3]{3}$, etc. It was only at the cost of a great effort that the French mathematician Liouville was able to find a few transcendental numbers in 1844. But the proof that the number π was transcendental, carried out by Lindemann in 1882, was a great mathematical event; indeed, it followed as a consequence that it was impossible to square the circle. And suddenly it became clear that the algebraic numbers met with at every step in mathematics are really extremely rare, while the transcendental numbers, so hard to construct, were really the common ones. After all, we have already seen that the algebraic numbers only form a countable set; while the set of all real numbers, as we only just demonstrated, is uncountable. This means that the difference between the real numbers and the algebraic numbers, i.e., the transcendental numbers, must also be uncountable.

The proof that transcendental numbers exist, carried out by G. Cantor in 1873, greatly impressed the mathematical world. Indeed, Cantor was able to demonstrate the existence of transcendental numbers without the need of constructing a single concrete example, using only general arguments. But the virtue of Cantor's proof was at the same time its weakness. It was impossible to deduce a rule from Cantor's reasoning which would allow the construction of even a single transcendental number, to say nothing of a test for the transcendence of such numbers as π or $2^{\sqrt{2}}$. His arguments constituted, as mathematicians say, a pure existence proof.

Long and Short Line Segments Have Equally Many Points

Unless the reader had been acquainted with the remarkable properties of infinite sets, the question "Are there more

points on a line segment 1 foot long or on a line segment
1 mile long?" would hardly have raised a shadow of doubt
in his mind. The answer was clear; there are many more
points on the segment of length 1 mile, for isn't it 5280
times longer? But by now, probably, the reader has learned
to beware of making categorical statements—the properties
of infinite sets are too dissimilar to what he has been taught
to expect by daily life.

And the long and short segments do in fact have equally
many points! In other words, it is possible to set up a one-
to-one correspondence between the points of these segments.
Figure 11 represents the easiest way of showing how this
can be done.

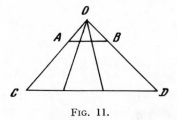

FIG. 11.

It is hard to reconcile oneself to the thought that a
path a million light years long has only as many points as
the radius of an atomic nucleus!

But even more unexpected is the result that there are
not even more points on the entire infinite line than on the
segment, i.e., a one-to-one correspondence can be set up
between the set of points on the line and the set of points
on the segment.

We do not even need the whole segment, but can discard
its endpoints (i.e., we use the open interval). It is clear
from Fig. 12 how to set up a one-to-one correspondence
between the interval and the line. It is clear that each point

on the interval corresponds to exactly one point on the line and that every point on the line has a mate on the interval.

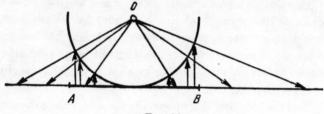

FIG. 12.

However, this correspondence can be set up in another way with the help of a curve—the tangent curve, the graph of the function $y = \tan x$ (Fig. 13).

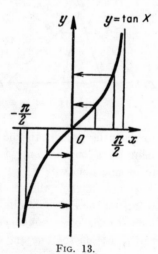

FIG. 13.

Segment and Square

Mathematicians reluctantly reconciled themselves with the fact that there are as many points on a segment as on an infinite line. But the following result of Cantor turned out to be even more unexpected. Searching for a set which would have more points than a segment, he turned to the set of points of a square. He had no doubt of the result— after all, the segment occupied in all only one side of the square, whereas the set of all segments which composed the square had the cardinality of the continuum.

Cantor searched for three years (from 1871 to 1874) for a proof that it was impossible to set up a one-to-one correspondence between the points of the segment and the points of the square.

The years went by, but the desired result could not be obtained. And then the completely unexpected happened. He succeeded in setting up the correspondence he believed impossible! He wrote to the mathematician Dedekind: "I see it, but I don't believe it."

But we have to resign ourselves to the fact that our intuition lets us down again here—it turns out that there are exactly as many points in the square as on the segment. A rigorous proof of the statement is made somewhat complicated by the lack of uniqueness of the decimal expansion of numbers. We shall therefore present only a sketch of Cantor's proof.

Let us take the segment $[0, 1]$ and the square of side 1. We may suppose that the square is situated as in Fig. 14. We have to set up a one-to-one correspondence between the points of the segment and the points of the square. Projection of the points of the square onto the segment AB will not help here; indeed, under projection an infinite set of points of the square are sent into one point of the segment (for example, all the points of segment DA go into point A).

We can solve the problem as follows: We can specify any point T of the square $ABCD$ by means of two numbers, its coordinates x and y (or more simply its distances along the sides AB and AD). These numbers can be written as

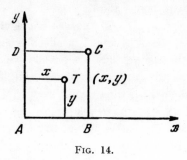

Fig. 14.

infinite decimals. Since x and y are not more than 1, these decimals have the form

$$x = 0.\,\alpha_1 \alpha_2 \ldots \alpha_n \ldots \qquad (3.26)$$

$$y = 0.\,\beta_1 \beta_2 \ldots \beta_n \ldots \qquad (3.27)$$

(for the sake of simplicity we do not take points lying on the sides of the square, but only take interior points). Here are the decimals of the numbers x and y, for example, if $x = 0.63205\ldots$ and $y = 0.21357\ldots$, then $\alpha_1 = 6$, $\alpha_2 = 3$, $\alpha_3 = 2$, etc, and $\beta_1 = 2$, $\beta_2 = 1$, $\beta_3 = 3$, etc.

Now we have to pick the point Q of the segment AB which is to correspond to T. It is enough to say what the length of the segment AQ is. We choose this length to be equal to the number z, whose decimal expansion is obtained by "shuffling" the decimal expansions of x and y. In other words, we form a third expansion from the two expansions (3.26) and (3.27) by combining their decimals.

$$z = 0.\,\alpha_1 \beta_1 \alpha_2 \beta_2 \alpha_3 \beta_3 \ldots \alpha_n \beta_n \ldots \qquad (3.28)$$

For instance, if

$$x = 0.515623\ldots \qquad (3.29)$$

and

$$y = 0.734856\ldots \tag{3.30}$$

then we obtain

$$z = 0.571354682536\ldots \tag{3.31}$$

The point z lies on the segment $[0, 1]$, and it is clear that different points of the square correspond to different points of the segment. Indeed, if points T and T' are not the same, then the decimal expansion of x and x' or y and y' must differ at least in one place. But this will lead to a difference in the decimal expansions of the numbers z and z'. A somewhat more detailed analysis shows that the corresponding points also do not coincide.

Thus we have set up a one-to-one correspondence between the points of the square and the points of a part of the segment $[0, 1]$. This shows that the set of points of the square has a cardinality no larger than that of the set of points of the segment. But its cardinality is certainly no smaller, so that the cardinalities must coincide.

Not just the square, but the cube as well has only as many points as the segment. In general, any geometric figure containing at least one line segment will have just as many points as the segment. Such sets are called sets with the cardinality of the *continuum* (from the Latin *continuum* — unbroken).

Somehow One Problem Does Not Work Out

We have now been acquainted for a while with two kinds of infinite sets. One kind has just as many elements as the set of natural numbers, and the other kind has just as many as the set of points of the line. We determined that there were more elements in the second set. It is now natural to ask ourselves the question: "Isn't there some set 'in between' which has more elements than the set of natural numbers and fewer elements than the set of points on the line?" This question has been given the name of the *continuum problem.* Many distinguished mathematicians have pondered it, starting with Georg Cantor himself, but the problem remained unsolved up to very recent times.

Academician N. N. Luzin, one of the most prominent mathematicians and the founder of the Soviet school of real variable theory, meditated on the continuum problem during the course of many years. But the solution was as elusive as a mirage in the desert (true, in the course of his reflections on this problem N. N. Luzin solved a whole series of the most difficult problems of set theory and founded a separate branch of mathematics—the descriptive theory of sets).

One day a fifteen-year-old boy Lev Shnizelman was brought in to N. N. Luzin. He was said to possess exceptional mathematical ability (later on he became one of the most prominent Soviet mathematicians and a corresponding member of the Academy of Sciences of the USSR). In order to test the capabilities of this young mathematician N. N. Luzin proposed that he solve thirty extremely difficult problems. He was able to do 29 of the problems, but one was... the continuum problem. Alas, at the end of a month the young mathematician came back to N. N. Luzin and sadly told him: "Somehow one problem doesn't work out."

The failure of the attempts to solve the continuum problem was not accidental. The situation here is reminiscent of the history of the parallel postulate. For two thousand years attempts were made to deduce this axiom from the remaining axioms of geometry. It became clear after the work of Lobachevsky, Hilbert, and other mathematicians that it did not contradict the other axioms, but could not be derived from them. Similarly, it became clear after the work of K. Gödel, P. S. Novikov, P. J. Cohen, and others that the assertion that there is no set of intermediate cardinality does not contradict the other axioms of set theory, but also cannot be derived from these axioms.

Is There a Set of Largest Cardinality?

Till now the largest cardinality we have become acquainted with is that of the set of points on the line, i.e., the cardinality of the continuum. Neither the set of points of the square nor the set of points of the cube has a larger cardinality. Perhaps the cardinality of the continuum is the largest possible? This turns out not to be the case. Indeed, there is no set of largest cardinality. Given any set A, there is a set of cardinality greater than the cardinality of A. We can construct it by associating to each point a of a set A the function $f^a(x)$ assuming the value 1 at this point and the value 0 at the remaining points. Clearly, distinct points give rise to distinct functions. For example, if set A consists of the points 1, 2, 3, then point 1 corresponds to a function which assumes the value 1 at this point, while point 2 corresponds to a function assuming the value 0 at point 1. These functions are distinct. We take our set B to be the set of all functions on A with values 0 and 1.

Thus, the cardinality of set B is not less than the cardinality of set A. Let us now show that these cardinalities are not equal, i.e., no one-to-one correspondence can be found between the elements of sets A and B. Indeed, suppose such a correspondence existed.

Let us then designate the function corresponding to element a of A by $f_a(x)$. Remember that all the functions $f_a(x)$ assume only the two values 0 and 1.

Let us define a new function $\varphi(x)$ by means of the equation:

$$\varphi(x) = 1 - f_x(x) \tag{3.32}$$

Thus, in order to determine the value of the function $\varphi(x)$ at some point a of A we first must find the function $f_a(x)$ corresponding to this point and subtract its value at $x = a$ from 1. It is now clear that the function $\varphi(x)$ is defined on the set A and assumes only the values 0 and 1. Consequently, $\varphi(x)$ is an element of set B. But then by our assumption $\varphi(x)$ corresponds to some point b of A; this means that

$$\varphi(x) = f_b(x) \tag{3.33}$$

It follows from Eqs. (3.32) and (3.33) that for all x in A

$$1 - f_x(x) = f_b(x) \tag{3.34}$$

Let us set $x = b$ in this equation. Then we get

$$1 - f_b(b) = f_b(b) \tag{3.35}$$

so that

$$f_b(b) = \tfrac{1}{2} \tag{3.36}$$

But this contradicts the requirement that the values of the function $f_b(x)$ be 0 and 1. The contradiction we have obtained shows that there can be no one-to-one correspondence between sets A and B.

Thus, given any set A, we can construct a set B of larger cardinality. Therefore, no set of largest cardinality can exist.

Let us note that the set B can be constructed in other ways. For instance, B can be taken to be the set of all subsets of set A. Indeed, let C be some subset of A. We choose a function $f(x)$ on A which assumes the value 1, if $x \in C$, and the value 0, if $x \notin C$. Clearly, distinct subsets give rise to distinct functions. On the other hand, each function $f(x)$ which assumes the values 0 and 1 corresponds to the subset of A composed of those elements x for which the function is 1. We have thus set up a one-to-one correspondence between the set of functions defined on set A and assuming the values 0 and 1 and the set of all subsets of A.

The Arithmetic of the Infinite

We have now learned something about the cardinalities of various sets. The concept of cardinality, as we mentioned earlier, is a generalization of the concept of number of elements in a finite set. Now, we can carry out certain arithmetic operations on the natural numbers—we can add, subtract and multiply them. These operations may be regarded as parallels of certain operations on sets. For example, the addition of natural numbers corresponds to the addition of two nonintersecting finite sets. If there are m elements in one set and n elements in the other, then there will be $m + n$ elements in their sum.

Operations on cardinalities are defined analogously. Here we shall employ special symbols to denote the cardinalities. For example, we denote the cardinality of a countable set by $\aleph_0$ ($\aleph$ is the first letter of the Hebrew alphabet and is called *aleph*). We denote the cardinality of the continuum by c (Gothic c), the cardinality of the set of all functions defined on the real axis by f, etc.

We can add cardinalities just as we add natural numbers. Namely, if the cardinality of set A is $\mathfrak{m}$ and the cardinality of set B is $\mathfrak{n}$, where A and B do not intersect, then $\mathfrak{m} + \mathfrak{n}$ denotes the cardinality of the set $A + B$. It follows from the properties of the addition of sets that

$$\mathfrak{m} + \mathfrak{n} = \mathfrak{n} + \mathfrak{m} \tag{3.37a}$$

$$\mathfrak{m} + (\mathfrak{n} + \mathfrak{p}) = (\mathfrak{m} + \mathfrak{n}) + \mathfrak{p} \tag{3.37b}$$

However, many of the rules of addition for infinite cardinalities are quite unlike the ordinary rules of arithmetic. But this is scarcely surprising, for we already know that the properties of infinite sets are quite different from those of finite sets. For example, in the arithmetic of the infinite we have the identities:

$$n + \aleph_0 = \aleph_0 \tag{3.38}$$

$$\aleph_0 + \aleph_0 = \aleph_0 \tag{3.39}$$

$$\aleph_0 + c = c \tag{3.40}$$

$$c + c = c \tag{3.41}$$

$$c + \mathfrak{f} = \mathfrak{f} \tag{3.42}$$

The first rule tells us that the sum of a finite and a countable set is a countable set; the second tells us that the sum of two countable sets is a countable set; the third tells us that when we supplement a set of cardinality that of the continuum by a countable set, we get a set with the cardinality of the continuum. The reader can now easily interpret the remaining identities.

Next let us see how infinite cardinalities multiply. We must first decide what set operation is related to multiplication of the natural numbers. Let A be a finite set composed of m elements and let B be a finite set containing n elements.

We form a new set $A + B$, whose elements are all possible pairs (a, b) with $a \in A$ and $b \in B$. If we let $a_1, \ldots, a_m$ denote the elements of the first set and $b_1, \ldots, b_n$ denote the elements of the second set, then these pairs can be arranged in the form of a tabulation:

$$
\begin{array}{c}
(a_1, b_1) \; \ldots \; (a_1, b_n) \\
\vdots \\
(a_m, b_1) \; \ldots \; (a_m, b_n)
\end{array}
\tag{3.43}
$$

It is clear from the tabulation that there are mn such pairs, i.e., they are equal in number to the product of the numbers m and n.

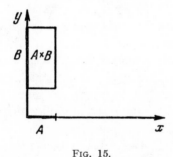

Fig. 15.

Let us carry this operation over to infinite sets. Let A and B be infinite sets. The set whose elements are all possible pairs (a, b), $a \in A$, $b \in B$, is called their direct product and denoted by $A \times B$. For example, if A is the set of points of segment $[0, 1]$ and B is the set of points of segment $[1, 3]$, then we can represent $A \times B$ by the set of points of the rectangle sketched in Fig. 15. Indeed, each point of the rectangle corresponds to its two projections on the axes.

If set A has cardinality $\mathfrak{m}$ and set B has cardinality $\mathfrak{n}$, then $\mathfrak{mn}$ denotes the cardinality of the set $A \times B$. We have the following rules for the multiplication of cardinalities:

$$\mathfrak{mn} = \mathfrak{nm} \tag{3.44}$$

$$(\mathfrak{mn})\mathfrak{p} = \mathfrak{m}(\mathfrak{np}) \tag{3.45}$$

$$\mathfrak{m}(\mathfrak{n} + \mathfrak{p}) = \mathfrak{mn} + \mathfrak{mp} \tag{3.46}$$

Furthermore, we have the identities

$$\aleph_0\aleph_0 = \aleph_0 \tag{3.47}$$

$$\aleph_0\mathfrak{c} = \mathfrak{c} \tag{3.48}$$

$$\mathfrak{cc} = \mathfrak{c} \tag{3.49}$$

The first identity means that if A and B are countable sets, then the set of all pairs (a, b), $a \in A$, $b \in B$, is also countable. This is another formulation of the statement that the sum of a countable set of countable sets is itself a countable set. And the identity $\mathfrak{cc} = \mathfrak{c}$ means that the numbers of points in the interval and in the square are one and the same. For $\mathfrak{c}$ is the number of points in the interval, while $\mathfrak{cc}$ is the number of points in the square.

Infinite Exponents

Since we already know how to multiply cardinalities together, we can raise a cardinality to any power given by a natural number. But now we are going to explain how to take powers of cardinalities when the exponent is infinite, that is we are going to explain what the symbol $\mathfrak{n}^{\mathfrak{m}}$ means. To do this we must again go back to finite sets and describe a set with n^m elements.

This can be done as follows: Let set A contain m elements and let set B contain n elements. B^A is to denote the set of all possible functions defined on the set A with values in the set B. In other words, each element of the set B^A gives us a rule for assigning an element $b = f(a)$ from B to each element a of A. Suppose, for example, that the set A consists of the three numbers 1, 2, 3 and set B consists of two elements: the dot and the dash. Then the elements of set B^A consist of "functions" like $f(1) = \cdot$, $f(2) = \cdot$, $f(3) = -$, or $f(1) = -$, $f(2) = \cdot$, $f(3) = \cdot$. These "functions" can be written simply as sequences of dots and dashes, each sequence having three symbols. It is easy to see that there are 8 such sequences, i.e., 2^3. Namely, we have the sequences:

$$\cdots \quad \cdot\cdot - \quad \cdot - \cdot \quad \cdot - - \qquad (3.50)$$
$$- \cdot\cdot \quad - \cdot - \quad - - \cdot \quad - - -$$

We found $8 = 2^3$ sequences. This is no accident. If the set A consists of m elements and the set B consists of n elements, then B^A contains n^m elements. We propose that the reader prove this for himself.

Now we are in a position to explain what we mean by the symbol n^m, where m and n are infinite cardinalities. Namely, we take a set A of cardinality m and a set B of cardinality n; we let B^A denote the set of all "functions" defined on A with values in B. n^m is the cardinality of this set.

We showed earlier that for any set A the cardinality of the set of functions defined on A with values 0 and 1 is greater than the cardinality of set A. This means that for any cardinality we have the inequality

$$2^m > m \qquad (3.51)$$

Let us note in addition that

$$c = 2^{\aleph_0} \qquad (3.52)$$

Indeed, we saw before that the set of all infinite telegrams had the cardinality of the continuum. But any infinite telegram is nothing more than a function defined on the set of natural numbers, which assumes only two values: dot and dash. Thus, the set of all infinite telegrams has cardinality $2^{\aleph_0}$. This proves equality (3.52).

On the Ordering of Numbers

The cardinalities of sets (or, as they are also called, *cardinal numbers*) do only half the work of the natural numbers. After all, the natural numbers can be applied to answer not only the question "how many?", but also to answer the question "in which place does it come?" In other words, we speak not only of "two," "five," "twenty," but also of "second," "fifth," "twentieth." But the cardinality tells us nothing about the order of the elements. And even though the set of natural numbers has as many elements as the set of integers, they are ordered in quite different ways. The set of natural numbers has a first element, while the set of integers has no first element.

The cardinal numbers therefore yield insufficient knowledge for the study of the order of arrangement of the elements in a set; we need new concepts for this purpose. We first introduce the concept of *ordered set*. We say that a set A is ordered, if for every pair of its elements a relation of inequality has been defined which possesses the following properties:

(1)   if $a < b$, then $a \neq b$;
(2)   if $a < b$ and $b < c$, then $a < c$.

It is easy to order the set of all real numbers, the set of all rational numbers, the set of all natural numbers, etc.

An ordering can also be introduced for the set of all complex numbers. Namely, we can say that $a + bi < c + di$, if either $a < c$, or $a = c$ and $b < d$. For example, $2 + 15i < 3 + 10i$, $2 + 4i < 2 + 5i$. The set of all polynomials can be ordered in an analogous fashion. Of course, different notions of ordering can be introduced into the same set.

For instance, consider the set of all the distinct words occurring in this book. This set might be ordered as follows: take the book and while reading it write down all the words appearing in it in the order in which you encounter them. In this case we can state the rule of ordering as follows: word A precedes word B, if word A is encountered earlier than word B when the book is read.

However, we can proceed in another way: agree that word A precedes word B if word A precedes word B in the alphabetical ordering. Clearly, these form two distinct ways of ordering the same set.

We say that two ordered sets A and B have the same *order type*, if we can set up a one-to-one correspondence between them which preserves the order of the elements. In other words, if $a_1 \leftrightarrow b_1$ and $a_2 \leftrightarrow b_2$, then $a_1 < a_2$ implies that $b_1 < b_2$.

For example, any two segments of the real line have the same order type. The mapping shown in Fig. 11 preserves the order of the points. The mapping of the whole line onto the open interval (the segment with endpoints removed) shown in Fig. 12 also preserves order. But the segment and the real line have different order types. Although we can set up a one-to-one correspondence between them, this correspondence must disturb the ordering—after all, the segment has initial and final points, while the line has none.

Completely Ordered Sets

Even countable sets can be ordered in the most varied ways.   Indeed, the sets of natural numbers, integers and rational numbers are countable and these sets are all ordered differently. The set of natural numbers has a first element (the number 1), while neither the set of integers nor the set of rational numbers has a first element. On the other hand, in both the sets of natural numbers and integers we can point out pairs of elements between which no other element of the set occurs (for example, the numbers 5 and 6), while in the set of rational numbers we can always find infinitely many elements of the set between any two elements.

In order to learn something about these varied orderings G. Cantor singled out a special class of ordered sets, some of whose properties were quite similar to those of the natural numbers. If we choose a nonempty subset of the natural numbers, then we can always find a least element, or leftmost element, among its members. G. Cantor gave the name of well-ordered sets to sets possessing this property. In other words, an ordered set A is said to be *well-ordered*, if each of its nonempty subsets has a first element.

As we have already indicated, the simplest example of a well-ordered set is the set of natural numbers.   We can represent it by means of the points 1, 2, 3,... on the half line $(0, \infty)$. Now, the mapping of the line onto the open interval shown in Fig. 12 preserves the order of the points. It maps the half line $(0, \infty)$ into the interval $(0, 1)$. Thus, we can choose points in the interval $(0, 1)$ instead of the points 1, 2, 3.... . We get an infinite set of points $a_1, a_2, \ldots, a_n, \ldots$ converging on the point 1 (Fig. 16a).

Now consider the point 1. We cannot use ordinary numbers to number this point—we have used these up in numbering the points $a_1, \ldots, a_n, \ldots$. We therefore need a new number, not a natural number, to index this point.

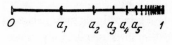

Fig. 16a.

Since the point 1 lies beyond all the points which we were able to index using the natural numbers, we call this new number "transfinite" (from the Latin meaning "beyond the finite"). The symbol ω has been adopted to denote the transfinite number immediately following the natural numbers $1, 2, 3, \ldots$. We therefore denote 1 by a_ω. The set A of all points $a_1, \ldots, a_n, \ldots, a_\omega$ is also a well ordered set. (Try to show this!)

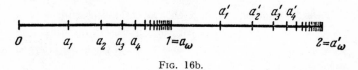

Fig. 16b.

We now shift all the points of set A one unit to the right. The point a_1 becomes point $a_1' = a_1 + 1$, point a_2 becomes point $a_2' = a_2 + 1$, etc. As a result we obtain a set B composed of the points $a_1', \ldots, a_n', \ldots, a_\omega'$. It is not difficult to show that the set $A + B$ is well ordered. Let us try to number its elements. We already know how to number the points of set A. Since point a_1' follows directly after point a_ω (Fig. 16b), it is natural to index it with the transfinite number $\omega + 1$, i.e., set $a_1' = a_{\omega+1}$. In the same way, it is natural to index the following point, i.e., a_2', with the transfinite number $\omega + 2$, etc. Now the point a_ω' comes after all the points $a_{\omega+1}, \ldots, a_{\omega+n}, \ldots$ so for it we use the transfinite number 2ω:

$$a_{\omega}' = a_{2\omega} \qquad (3.53)$$

The reader has probably already guessed that we are now going to shift the points of set A two units to the right in order to get the new points which we will have to index with the transfinite numbers $2\omega+1, \ldots, 2\omega+n, \ldots, 3\omega$. Continuing in this way, we find a well-ordered set composed of points indexed by transfinite numbers of the form $k\omega+n$, where k and n are natural numbers.

But this does not complete the construction of transfinite numbers. We have again obtained a set distributed over the half line $(0, \infty)$, and infinitely many points of our set are located on each segment $[n, m+1]$. Let us now again map the half line $(0, \infty)$ on the interval $(0, 1)$. We get a set of points converging to the point 1. We again need a new transfinite number to index the point 1; this time it will be ω^2. We can now go on to construct the transfinite numbers $\omega^2+1, \ldots, \omega^3, \ldots, \omega^n, \ldots$ and even ω^{ω}. There is even a transfinite number:

But we are not going to dwell any longer on these questions.

The Enigmatic Axiom

We have already said that some sets can be ordered in different ways. But is it always possible to order a given set;

and if it is always possible, can the set always be made into a well-ordered set? Many mathematicians have worked on this problem—after all, it follows that if the answer is yes, any set can be indexed with the help of transfinite numbers.

An unexpectedly simple and short solution was published in 1904 by Zermelo—he was able to show that any set can be well ordered (G. Cantor had already conjectured this in 1883). However, Zermelo's proof did not satisfy all mathematicians. The problem was that the proof depended on one assumption which appeared to be far from obvious to both its author and others. This statement came to be called the *axiom of choice* or *Zermelo's axiom* and can be illustrated as follows:

Suppose that in front of you lay several piles of apples. It is obvious that you could select an apple from each pile and put them in a new pile. It would also seem to be true that the same could be done if there were infinitely many apples in each pile as well as infinitely many piles. This is what constitutes the axiom of choice:

If an infinite set of infinite sets is given, then it is possible to choose one element from each set without giving the rule of choice in advance.

Indeed, all the trouble arises from these last words—the axiom of choice leads to completely nonconstructive proofs: with it you can prove, for example, that every set can be well ordered, but it does not give any information about how to go about it.

Mathematicians employed the axiom of choice for many years, considering it to be completely obvious. But when they began to reflect on it more deeply, it came to appear more and more mysterious. Many of the theorems proved with the help of the axiom of choice completely contradict our mathematical intuition. This led the well-known mathematician Bertrand Russell to speak of this axiom as follows:

"At first it seems obvious, but the more you think about it, the stranger the deductions from this axiom seem to become; in the end you cease to understand what is meant by it."

Nevertheless, the majority of mathematicians make use of the axiom of choice in their studies without any qualms.

Two Apples from One

Let us talk about one of the most surprising consequences of the axiom of choice. Probably everyone has seen a clever magician at work on the stage. First he shows the spectators an empty sack, then he drops a ball into the sack, only to draw out ... two; dropping in the two balls, he pulls out four; dropping in the four, he pulls out eight. Of course, everyone knows that it is no miracle, but is simply "sleight of hand." Such miracles can, however, happen in the theory of sets.

We take an ordinary apple and divide it in any way into four pieces. It seems clear that if we take only two of the pieces, it will not be possible to form an entire apple from them (in the same way, if you have eaten half an orange, you cannot form an entire orange from the remaining slices).

However, mathematicians can divide a sphere into four equal parts in such a way that an entire sphere of the same radius can be formed from two of the parts, without supplementing them in any way, simply by translating them as rigid bodies. A second, identical sphere can be formed from the other two parts. Thus, we can obtain two distinct spheres from the one. It is a pity that this problem is only capable of being solved in theory, otherwise we could make two apples from one, then four, then eight, etc. Of course, the problem cannot be solved in the real world—it would contradict the law of conservation of matter.

FIG. 17.

Such a division of the sphere into four parts is based on the axiom of choice.

At this time we shall not speak further of other, equally strange consequences of this axiom.

4

Remarkable Functions and Curves, or a Stroll through a Mathematical Art Museum

How the Notion of Function Developed

The majority of mathematical concepts underwent a long period of development. They first arose as generalizations of intuitive ideas derived from everyday experience. With gradual removal of special and accidental aspects, these intuitive ideas slowly crystallized into exact mathematical definitions. But it often happened that these definitions applied not only to those objects whose study led to their formulation, but also to other objects that had not been thought about earlier. The study of these new objects was begun and the process of abstraction was carried to ever higher levels; next came the extension of the original definitions on the basis provided by the studies. Ever broader meaning came to be attributed to mathematical concepts; they embraced wider and wider classes of objects, occurring in more varied fields of mathematics.

The concept of number, for example, underwent such a long period of development, starting in prehistoric times when people could only count "one, two, many," and, carrying on to our own time: natural numbers, fractions, negative numbers, complex numbers, quaternions, hypercomplex numbers,.... And it must be admitted that not every new generalization of this or that concept was enthusiastically received by all mathematicians. For example, for a long time not only the complex but even the negative numbers were not recognized as real by many mathematicians.

The notion of function also followed a tortuous path. The idea of the interdependence of two quantities apparently arose in classical Greek science. But here the quantities were only of a geometric nature. Even Newton, one of the founders of mathematical analysis, employed only geometric language in his discussion of interdependent quantities. Although the notion of function had actually been in use since the days of Fermat and Descartes, the term "function" itself only came into being in 1694, first appearing in the works of the German mathematician Leibniz. He and Newton share the credit for the foundations of the calculus. But Leibniz's notion of function was a very narrow one: he named the abscissa, ordinate, subtangent and subnormal, radius of curvature and other line segments related to a definite point on a curve, and said that a certain kind of dependence existed between any two of these. Thus, Leibniz too restricted function to the realm of geometry. It was only in 1718 that Leibniz's student J. Bernoulli gave a definition of function free of geometric language:

A function of a variable quantity is a magnitude formed in some manner from this variable quantity and constants.

The next step in the development of the concept of function is linked to the name of Leonhard Euler of the Petersburg Academy, a brilliant student of J. Bernoulli. He defined function thus in his "Differential Calculus":

Quantities dependent on others such that as the second change, so do the first, are said to be functions.

However, Euler and the other mathematicians of his time required that a function must be expressible by means of a formula. From the point of view of the mathematicians of the 18th century the expression:

$$y = \begin{cases} x, & \text{if } x < 0 \\ x^2, & \text{if } x > 0 \end{cases} \tag{4.1}$$

defines not one, but two functions.

It soon became clear that the matter was significantly more complex. When he solved the problem of the vibrating string, D. Bernoulli obtained an answer in the form of what is called a *trigonometric series*. We shall not discuss these here, but only say that the shape of the string is given by a single formula (although one containing an infinite number of terms).

This same problem of the vibrating string was solved by the French mathematician d'Alembert. d'Alembert's solution had a form quite different from that of Bernoulli's, and, what is most important, could be given by different formulas for different values of the argument.

What looked to be an insoluble contradiction now loomed up before 18th century mathematics: two answers had been obtained for the same problem, one expressed by a single formula for all values of the argument and another by several formulas. D. Bernoulli's solution was questioned because of this: it was thought that he had not found all solutions to the problem, just the solutions expressible in a single formula. A bitter controversy arose in which all the prominent mathematicians of the 18th century, Euler, d'Alembert, and others, took part.

The controversy, in essence, was over the concept of function, the connection between the functional dependence and the possibility of expressing this dependence by means of a formula. A definitive solution to the question was obtained at the beginning of the 19th century, when the French mathematician J. Fourier showed that the sum of an infinite series of trigonometric functions can be expressed by different formulas over different intervals. He then gave a new definition of function, stressing that the main thing was the assignment of values for the function; whether this assignment was carried out by means of a single formula or not was unimportant.

Fourier's result was refined by the German mathematician Dirichlet, who showed that any given curve could be the graph of the sum of a trigonometric series. It was required only that the number of maxima and minima on the curve be finite and that the curve be finite and bounded in amplitude. Dirichlet also refined Fourier's definition of function and gave it the form in which it is employed today (quite similar definitions were given somewhat earlier than Dirichlet's by Lacroix, Lobachevsky, and other mathematicians). Dirichlet's definition reads:

A variable quantity y is said to be a function of a variable quantity x, if to each value of the quantity x there corresponds a uniquely determined value of the quantity y.

Later on the words "belonging to some set" were added to the words "each value of the quantity x" (after all, the function does not have to be defined for all values of x).

This definition was extremely general: not a word was said about the necessity of giving the function by means of a single formula holding over the whole domain of definition. Moreover, it need not even be given by any formula at all but could be defined in words. For example, Dirichlet himself studied the function:

$$f(x) = \begin{cases} 0, & \text{if } x \text{ is an irrational number} \\ 1, & \text{if } x \text{ is a rational number} \end{cases} \tag{4.2}$$

This definition did not specify a function according to the viewpoint of 18th century mathematicians; for no formula was given which would allow one to compute the values of *Dirichlet's function*. Nevertheless, this definition completely determines the function. It is quite clear that, for example, $f(\frac{3}{4}) = 1$ while $f(\sqrt{2}) = 0$.

Dirichlet's definition, in essence, was definitive (with the indicated refinement) for numerical functions of a numerical argument. Further developments consisted in considering functions defined on arbitrary sets and assuming their values on arbitrary sets. Indeed, suppose we are given two sets A and B and suppose that an element b of B has been placed in correspondence with each element a of A. Then we say that a function has been defined on set A with values in set B. In this very general formulation, the notion of function merges with those of *correspondence*, mapping and transformation.

For example, from this point of view the area of a triangle is a function defined on the set of all triangles and assuming its values in the set of positive numbers. And the circle inscribed in a triangle is a function defined on the set of all triangles with values in the set of circles. But here we are not going to maintain such a general viewpoint; we shall restrict our interest to functions defined on sets of numbers and assuming numerical values.

The Genie Escapes from the Bottle

Dirichlet's definition allows functions to have very odd properties. Before, if one wanted to construct a function with some unusual property, one had to spend a long time combining different formulas, but now the job was much simpler. It was now possible to construct and study various functions without worrying about whether they could be expressed by formulas. And for the last half century functions have been constructed with properties completely at variance with those of the "well-behaved" functions. Truly, even Dirichlet himself did not believe that such "monsters" could exist.

Dirichlet's own function, of which we spoke earlier, was already unusual. After all, there are infinitely many rational and irrational numbers on even the smallest interval of the x axis. But Dirichlet's function is one for rational numbers and zero for irrational numbers. Thus, as we move along the x axis, the value of the function constantly jumps back and forth between 0 and 1. It is impossible to graph this function, since it is discontinuous at every point.

And even among the continuous functions are some with unexpected properties. For example, can a continuous function have infinitely many maxima and minima on a finite interval? This seems impossible at first glance. After all, the curve has to take up space in falling from a maximum to a minimum, then again rising to a maximum, etc. How can it do all this in a finite interval? Nevertheless, such odd functions do exist and it is quite simple to construct one.

We shall construct such a function on the segment $[0, 1]$. We first cut the segment in two and construct an equilateral triangle on the left half. Now we divide the right half into two equal parts and construct a second equilateral triangle on the segment $[\frac{1}{2}, \frac{3}{4}]$. We carry out the described operation infinitely many times. As a result we find a mountain range with infinitely many peaks gradually dropping down to the point 1 (Fig. 18). We take the curve obtained as the graph of the function $f(x)$. Thus, the function is defined at each point of the segment $[0, 1]$ with the exception of the right endpoint 1. Here we put $f(1) = 0$.

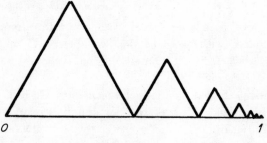

0 1

FIG. 18.

Since the height of the peaks approaches 0 as x approaches 1, we obtain a function continuous at all points of the segment $[0, 1]$. But the number of maxima and minima on this segment is infinite!

In order to construct such a strange function a mathematician of the 18th century would have to spend a lot of time trying out combinations of functions before he would conjecture that the function

$$f(x) = \begin{cases} x \cos \dfrac{\pi}{x}, & \text{if } x \neq 0 \\[2mm] 0, & \text{if } x = 0 \end{cases} \tag{4.3}$$

had infinitely many maxima and minima on the segment [0, 1] (Fig. 19).

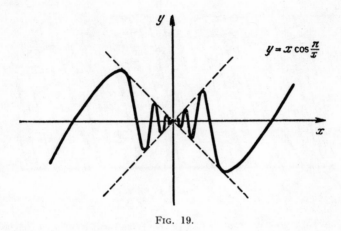

$$y = x \cos \frac{\pi}{x}$$

FIG. 19.

But functions with infinitely many maxima and minima were only the first of the unpleasant surprises in store for mathematicians. The genie had only begun to escape from the bottle.

Wet Points

The function we constructed in the preceding section had only one point near which there were infinitely many maxima and minima; this was the point 1. Now we shall construct another function with many more such points.

Imagine that rain is falling on the segment [0, 1] of the *x* axis. We go about providing shelter from the rain as follows. We divide the segment [0, 1] into three equal parts and erect a tent in the form of an equilateral triangle in the central part. It protects all the points of the central

part from the rain (except the endpoints, i.e., the points
$\frac{1}{3}$ and $\frac{2}{3}$).

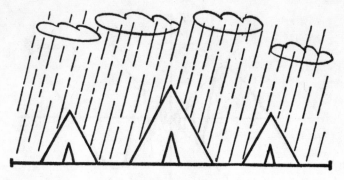

FIG. 20.   It is raining.

Now we divide each of the two pieces left over into three
parts and protect the central part with a tent of the same
form (but only half as wide).   We now have the curve
sketched in Fig. 21.   In the third step of this procedure we
erect four more tents, then eight more, etc.

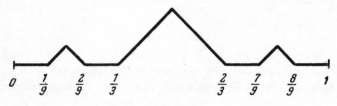

FIG. 21.

Now we come to the question of whether all the points of
the segment have been sheltered by the saw-toothed curve,
or whether there remain points wet by the rain?   It is easy
to point out some of the "wet" points—these are the endpoints of the sheltered segments (i.e., such points as 1/3,

2/3, 1/9, 2/9, 7/9, 8/9, etc.). All these points were left unprotected when the corresponding tents were erected, and
they remain unprotected by the tents erected subsequently.
It is easy to see that there are infinitely many such endpoints,
but that they still form only a countable set.

But it turns out that there is an uncountable set of "wet"
points in addition to these. It is convenient to use the
ternary representation in order to describe them. As we
know, the ternary representation is formed in the same way
as the decimal representation, except that the numbers are
grouped in threes instead of tens. Thus, in the ternary
representation we only employ the three digits 0, 1, 2 for
writing numbers in place of the ten ordinarily used.

It is easy to learn how to change the representation of a
number whose ternary representation is

$$0.02020202\ldots$$

It is represented in the decimal system by the infinite
geometric progression:

$$\frac{2}{3^2} + \frac{2}{3^4} + \frac{2}{3^6} + \ldots \tag{4.4}$$

The sum of this progression is $\frac{1}{4}$. Thus,

$$\tfrac{1}{4} = 0.020202\ldots \tag{4.5}$$

Now we can say exactly which points remain wet after
all the protective tents have been set up. The first tent
shelters the points lying between $\frac{1}{3}$ and $\frac{2}{3}$. But these are
just the points whose ternary representations have the form

$$0.1\ldots \tag{4.6}$$

where the dots stand for any combination of digits 0, 1, 2
(in the same way that all the points whose decimal representa-

tions begin with the digit 1, i.e., have the form 0.1..., lie between the points 1/10 and 2/10).

Those points still wet after the first step are those whose ternary representations have the form

$$0.0\ldots \qquad (4.7)$$

or the form

$$0.2\ldots \qquad (4.8)$$

We can prove in the same way that after the two tents of the second step have been set up the points remaining wet are only those whose ternary representations begin with one of the following four combinations:

$$0.00\ldots$$
$$0.02\ldots$$
$$0.20\ldots \qquad (4.9)$$
$$0.22\ldots$$

Thus, any point in whose ternary representation a one occurs will at some stage be protected from the rain. In the end only those points remain wet whose ternary representations can be written without using 1. For example, the points

$$\tfrac{1}{4} = 0.020202\ldots \qquad (4.10)$$

and

$$\tfrac{3}{4} = 0.20202\ldots \qquad (4.11)$$

remain wet.

But now it must be clear why the set of "wet" points has the cardinality of the continuum. After all, this set

can be put into one-to-one correspondence with the set of
infinite telegrams [see (3.20)]. We can do this by putting
each point of the form

$$0.20220200\ldots \qquad (4.12)$$

in correspondence with an infinite telegram by replacing 0
by the dot and 2 by the dash. Different numbers correspond
to different telegrams when this procedure is followed. We
already know that the set of infinite telegrams has the
cardinality of the continuum; thus, the set of wet points
will also have this cardinality.

The set of points we called wet was first constructed by
Cantor, and is now called *Cantor's set*. It is clear from the
construction of the tents that there are infinitely many
maxima and minima of the saw-toothed curve near each
point of Cantor's set.

The Devil's Staircase

There is still another interesting function related to
Cantor's set. It is defined as follows. We first divide the
segment [0, 1] into three equal parts and stipulate that our
function equal $\frac{1}{2}$ at each point of the middle third. Then
we divide the left and right thirds into three equal parts
and stipulate that the function equal 1/4 from 1/9 to 2/9,
and equal 3/4 from 7/9 to 8/9. We now have four segments
on which the function is not yet defined:

$$\left[0, \frac{1}{9}\right] \qquad \left[\frac{2}{9}, \frac{1}{3}\right] \qquad \left[\frac{2}{3}, \frac{7}{9}\right] \qquad \left[\frac{8}{9}, 1\right] \qquad (4.13)$$

We divide each of these into three equal parts and set the
function equal to 1/8, 3/8, 5/8, 7/8, respectively, on the four
middle pieces.

Continuing this process, we obtain a function which is
defined on all the "dry" points, i.e., on all the points not
belonging to Cantor's set. It is easy to define it on the
points of this set too, and in such a way that it becomes
continuous and nondecreasing on the segment $[0, 1]$. An
approximation to the graph of the function obtained is
shown in Fig. 22. It has the form of a staircase with an
infinite number of steps (not all the steps are shown on the
graph).

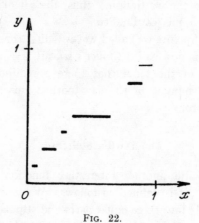

FIG. 22.

Of course, after learning about curves with infinitely
many maxima and minima, we are not likely to be surprised
at a staircase with an infinite number of steps. But here is
something surprising. Let us compute the total length of
our staircase. The first step has length $1/3$, the next two
have length $1/9$ apiece, the next four have length $1/27$
apiece, etc. Thus, the sum of the lengths of all the steps
is expressed by the infinite geometric progression:

$$\frac{1}{3} + \frac{2}{9} + \frac{4}{27} + \cdots \qquad (4.14)$$

The sum of this progression is

$$\frac{\frac{1}{3}}{1 - \frac{2}{3}} = 1 \qquad (4.15)$$

Hence, the total length of the staircase is 1. But the function does not increase at all along these steps; all its rising is concentrated at the points of Cantor's set. But very "few" points fall to the share of this set—even though its cardinality is that of the continuum, its length is zero! (The length of the segment [0, 1] is 1 and the total length of the steps is 1). Thus, our function manages somehow to rise from 0 to 1, even though it only increases on a set of zero length and never makes any jumps! Isn't this really surprising?

A Prickly Curve

For a period extending over many centuries mathematicians dealt only with curves at each point of which a tangent could be constructed. If there were exceptions these occurred at only a few points. The curve seemed to break

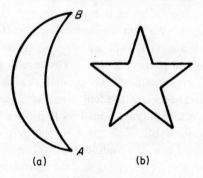

(a)   (b)

FIG. 23.

at these points, and they were therefore called *points of fracture*. The curve drawn in Fig. 23a has *two points of fracture*, while the curve drawn in Fig. 23b has ten *points of fracture*.

But the curve that we just now constructed already has infinitely many *points of fracture*: the curve in Fig. 19 has a countable set of such points, while the curve in Fig. 20 has a whole continuum of them. It breaks at each point of the Cantor set and, in addition, at the peaks of all the triangles. However, even the curve of Fig. 21 has breaks on a comparatively "small" set of points: its length is zero.

For a long time no mathematician believed that there could exist a continuous curve wholly composed of "saw-teeth," "breaks" and "prickles." Mathematicians were greatly amazed, therefore, when someone succeeded in constructing such a curve, and what is more, a function with a graph like a picket fence. The first to do this was the Czech mathematician Bolzano. But his work remained unpublished for a long time, and the first published example was that of the German mathematician K. Weierstrass. However, it is difficult for us to present Weierstrass' example, for it is based on the theory of trigonometric series.

We shall now discuss Bolzano's example, making a few slight changes. We first divide the segment $[0, 1]$ into four equal parts and construct an isosceles right triangle over the two central parts (Fig. 24a). The resulting curve is the graph of some function which we shall denote by $y = f_1(x)$. We next divide each of the four pieces again into four equal parts and correspondingly construct four more isosceles right triangles (Fig. 24b). This gives us the graph of a second function $y = f_2(x)$. If we add these two functions, the graph of the sum $y = f_1(x) + f_2(x)$ has the form sketched in Fig. 24c. It is clear that this curve already has more breaks and that these breaks are more densely distributed. In the next stage we again divide each piece into four parts, now constructing 16 isosceles right triangles and then adding the corresponding function $y = f_3(x)$ to the function $y = f_1(x) + f_2(x)$.

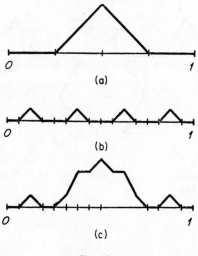

Fig. 24.

As we continue this process, we obtain a curve with a larger and larger number of breaks. In the limit we obtain a curve with a break at each point and possessing a tangent at no point.

A similar example of a curve possessing a tangent at no point was constructed by the Dutch mathematician Van der Waerden. He took an equilateral triangle, divided each of its sides into three equal parts and then constructed new equilateral triangles with peaks pointing out over the three central sections. This gave him a figure something like a sixpointed star (Fig. 25a). He then went on to divide each of the twelve sides of this star into three equal parts, again constructing equilateral triangles. This gave the even more prickly curve drawn in Fig. 25b. After infinitely many divisions and constructions of right triangles he obtained a curve at each point of which there was a break or a prickle.

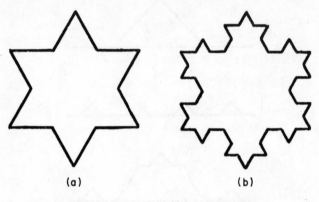

(a)   (b)

FIG. 25.

Mathematicians constructed many continuous functions whose graphs possess a tangent at no point and began to study their properties. These properties have no similarity to those of the "well-behaved" smooth functions with which they had dealt up to that time. It is no wonder, then, that mathematicians trained in the classical tradition regarded these new functions with astonishment. Going even beyond this, the prominent exponent of classical analysis Charles Hermite wrote as follows to his friend, the Dutch mathematician Stieltjes:

"I turn away in horror from this regrettable plague of continuous functions that do not have a derivative at even one point" (i.e., as we have named them, everywhere prickly curves).

The famous French mathematician H. Poincaré wrote:

"In the old days there was some practical purpose behind the search for new functions. Now functions are invented

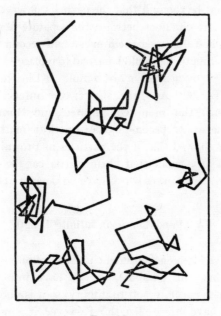

Fig. 26.

specifically for pointing up gaps in the reasoning of our predecessors; no other conclusion can be drawn from them except this."

But the later development of the science showed Poincaré to be wrong. In physics we encounter curves highly reminiscent of the everywhere prickly curves of Van der Waerden and others. These curves are the trajectories of particles undergoing Brownian motion caused by collisions with molecules. The French scientist Fr. Peppin made a sketch of the motion of these particles. He observed their positions every 30 seconds and connected the points thus obtained with straight line segments. His result was a tangle of broken lines something like that sketched in Fig. 26. But it should not be thought that the particles observed actually moved in straight lines between the separate observations. If Peppin had observed them every half second instead of every half minute, he would have had to replace each straight line segment by a much more complicated broken line like that in Fig. 26. And the shorter the interval between observations, the more complicated and "prickly" the broken line would become. The American mathematician N. Wiener showed that if the particles in Brownian motion are sufficiently small that their inertia can be neglected, they move along curves which have no tangent at any point.

A Closed Curve of Infinite Length

We have often encountered curves of infinite length: the straight line, the parabola, etc all have infinite length. But all these curves go off to infinity, so it is not surprising that they have infinite length. However, it is not difficult to construct a curve entirely contained in a finite region of the plane and still having infinite length. For this we can take a circle and wind a spiral with infinitely many turns around it (Fig. 27). Since the number of turns is infinite and the length of each turn is greater than that of the circumference of the circle, the length of the spiral must be infinite.

But can we construct a closed curve of infinite length?
The ordinary closed curves: the circle, the ellipse, the

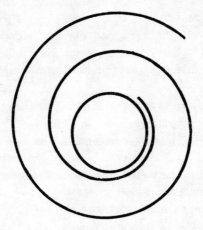

FIG. 27.

cardioid (Fig. 28) all have finite length. However, the length
of Van der Waerden's prickly curve is infinite.

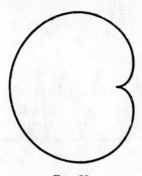

FIG. 28.

Indeed, the perimeter of the original triangle is **3**. As
is easily computed, the star obtained in the first stage has

length 4. And in the following stage we obtain a curve composed of 48 segments each of length 1/9. Thus its perimeter is 48/9. Next we obtain a curve of length 192/27, etc. In general, at nth stage we obtain a curve with perimeter $3 \cdot (\frac{4}{3})^n$. But this expression approaches infinity as n increases, so that the length of Van der Waerden's curve is infinite.

There are still other curves of infinite length. We construct the following curve as an example. We divide the segment $[0, 1]$ in half and construct an isosceles triangle of altitude 1 on the left half. Next we divide the half $[\frac{1}{2}, 1]$ into two equal parts and construct an isosceles triangle of altitude $\frac{1}{2}$ on the leftmost piece $[\frac{1}{2}, \frac{3}{4}]$. We construct the next isosceles triangle, again with altitude $\frac{1}{2}$, on the segment $[3/4, 7/8]$; the next four triangles are constructed with altitude $\frac{1}{4}$, etc (Fig. 29).

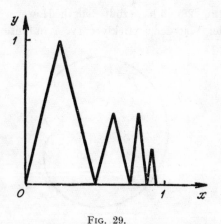

F$_{IG}$. 29.

We again get a descending chain of mountains as in Fig. 18. But here the chain descends very slowly. It is clear that the length of each lateral side of the first triangle is greater than 1, of those of the second and third are greater than $\frac{1}{2}$, of those of the fourth, fifth, sixth, and seventh are greater than $\frac{1}{4}$, etc (the length of the lateral side is always greater than the altitude). Thus the length of the broken line is not less than the sum of the infinite series:

$$2 + \left(\frac{2}{2} + \frac{2}{2}\right) + \left(\frac{2}{4} + \frac{2}{4} + \frac{2}{4} + \frac{2}{4}\right) + \ldots \quad (4.16)$$

But the sum of the numbers within each parenthetical expression is 2, and the number of parentheses is infinite; hence the sum of the series and the length of our curve are infinite.

A Mathematical Carpet

They tell how once Catherine the Second asked one of her generals what was the difference between a mortar and a howitzer. The embarassed general replied: "You see, Queenmother, a mortar is one thing and a howitzer is something else." We would probably receive an informative answer like this one if we were to ask a person knowing little about mathematics what is the difference between a curve, a surface, and a solid. Moreover, he would be surprised that we asked about such obvious things. After all, it is quite clear that a curve, a surface, and a solid are quite different things, and no one would call a circle a surface or a sphere a curve.

But a witty chess master once said that the difference between a master and a beginning chess player is that the beginner has everything clearly fixed in mind, while to the master everything is a mystery. That is also how matters

stand with our question. Of course, when we are speaking
of such geometric figures as a square or a circle, no one has
any doubts about which is a curve and which is a surface.
But in the course of mathematical development, since
Cantor's discoveries, there have appeared many queer
geometric figures, and even an experienced, knowledgeable
professor, not to speak of a student, will not be able to decide
right away whether they are curves, surfaces, or solids.

We shall present some of these figures. We take the
segment [0, 1], divide it in two and erect a perpendicular of
length $\frac{1}{2}$ at the center of the segment. Next we again divide
each of the halves in two and construct a perpendicular, this
time of length $\frac{1}{4}$, at each of the new points of division. Then
we again divide the sections obtained into 2 parts and erect
perpendiculars of length $\frac{1}{8}$ at the points of division.

FIG. 30.

After five such steps we obtain the figure drawn in
Fig. 30. But we will not stop after five steps, but will
continue our operation infinitely many times. The result
is some geometric figure. Well, then, what is it, a curve
or a surface? After all, we erected an infinite number of
perpendiculars. Don't they solidify and fill up a small
bit of surface near the segment [0, 1]? It is not too easy to
answer this question.

And here is another example. We take a square of side 1 and divide it into 9 equal parts; then we discard the central part (leaving the sides of the discarded square). After this we divide each of the remaining squares into 9 equal squares, and again discard the central squares. After one more such operation we arrive at the figure drawn in Fig. 31 (the squares

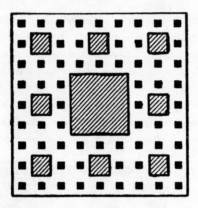

Fig. 31.

to be discarded are cross-hatched). It is clear that the figure in Fig. 31 is still a surface. But we will not stop at the third step; the squares will be divided into nine equal parts infinitely many times, and each time the central part will be discarded. In the end we obtain a geometric figure called *Sierpinski's carpet* after the Polish mathematician who devised it.

The figure looks like cloth woven by some mad weaver. The thread, frame and woof come from far and wide to be woven into a very symmetric and beautiful design. But the resulting carpet is full of holes—there is not an uncut piece in it; even the smallest square had to have its center cut out.

And it is not at all clear whether this carpet is a curve or a surface. After all, on the one hand, it does not contain a single solid piece, and so can hardly be called a surface; but, on the other hand, the threads forming it were woven into such a complex pattern that probably no one would unhesitatingly call Sierpinski's carpet a curve. In any case, it would be very hard to draw this "curve."

But Sierpinski's carpet is not the most complicated geometric figure. Instead of a square we could have taken a cube, divided it into 27 equal small cubes and discarded the central small cube along with its 6 neighboring cubes. Then we would have divided each small remaining cube into 27 equal parts and again would have carried out the operation of discarding certain parts (the solid remaining after two such operations is shown in Fig. 32). Suppose that the opera-

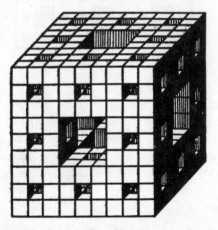

Fig. 32.

tion had been carried out infinitely many times. What kind of a figure would we get after all the pieces had been discarded—a curve, a surface or a solid?

Euclid Does Not Rely on Euclid

When a complicated geometric problem was placed before mathematicians of an earlier time, they first proceeded to examine what Euclid had written about it. After all, for almost two thousand years Euclid was the standard of mathematical rigor and an encyclopaedia of geometric knowledge. It is significant that even philosophers striving to secure themselves from reproach regarding the rigor of their arguments, had recourse to Euclid's language and formulated their statements as axioms, lemmas, and theorems.

But as far as our question is concerned, everything Euclid wrote was entirely too vague. The first lines of Euclid's book "Elements" read as follows:

1. A point is that which has no parts.
2. A curve is length without width.
3. The extremity of a curve is a point.
4. A surface is that which has only length and width.
5. The extremity of a surface is a curve.
6. A boundary is that which is the extremity of something.
7. A figure is that which is contained within something or within some boundaries.

Now, like these or not, they are not rigorous mathematical definitions. A person not knowing what points, curves, or lines are will hardly get much useful information from these "definitions," so reminiscent of the answer of the confused general ("a curve is one thing, and a surface is something else"). And, in any case, we shall not succeed in finding out from these definitions whether Sierpinski's carpet is a curve or a surface, whether it has just length without width or both length and width.

However, such complicated figures as Sierpinski's carpet were unknown in Euclid's time, and definitions were not really necessary for simple figures—everyone could pick out which were the curves and which were the surfaces in a figure. It seems, though, that Euclid himself felt that all was not right with his definitions of the fundamental concepts. In any case, having presented these definitions in the beginning of the book, he went on to completely forget about them and did not employ them even once in the remainder of his work.

Are Rigorous Definitions Needed?

Euclid's authority stood unquestioned during the course of two thousand years. To doubt his statements in any way was to decisively and irrevocably undermine your own mathematical reputation. One of the greatest mathematicians of the 19th century, Karl Friedrich Gauss, arrived at the idea of a non-Euclidean geometry even before Lobachevsky, but did not publish his investigations, fearing, as he wrote one friend, the screams of the Boeotians.* It was finally the mathematical exploit of the great Russian geometer Nikolai Ivanovich Lobachevsky, who did publish his discoveries in spite of the derision of the uncomprehending savants, that gave the world non-Euclidean geometry.

It became clear after the appearance of N. I. Lobachevsky's work that there existed two geometries, both irreproachable logically, but arriving at entirely different theorems. But if this is so, then every appeal to "geometric obviousness" completely lost its value. Each geometric assertion now had to be based on rigorous definitions and irreproachable

---

* A proverbially dull Greek tribe.

logical arguments. And now it was especially important that the fundamental geometric concepts of curve, figure, and solid be given exact definitions, in no way like those of the type "this is one thing, and that is something else."

This attempt at rigorous definition characterized not only the geometry, but also the analysis of the 19th century.

Science had succeeded in solving the most varied problems, from calculating the trajectory of an artillery shell to predicting the motions of planets and comets, with the aid of the differential and integral calculus based on the work of Newton, Leibniz, Euler, Lagrange, and other great mathematicians of the 17th and 18th centuries. But the fundamental concepts with whose aid these remarkable results were achieved were defined in a highly unrigorous manner. The mathematical analysis of that time was based on the concept of infinitesimal quantity, something balancing on the border of existence and nonexistence; something like zero, but not really zero. And mathematicians of the 18th century were forced to encourage their dubious students with the words: "Work, and belief will come to you."

But, really, mathematics is not religion; it cannot be founded on faith. And what was most important, the methods yielding such remarkable results in the hands of the great masters began to lead to errors and paradoxes when employed by their less talented students. The masters were kept from error by their perfect mathematical intuition, that subconscious feeling that often leads to the right answer more quickly than lengthy logical reasoning. But the students did not possess this intuition, and the end of the 18th century was marked by an unprecedented scandal in mathematics—an influx of formulas worth less than the paper they were printed on and questionable theorems whose domain of applicability was entirely unclear.

So, like children who break a beautiful toy in order to see what makes it work, the mathematicians of the 19th century subjected to a severe critique all the concepts employed up to that time and then began to rebuild mathematics on a foundation of rigorous definitions. Appeals to intuition were rejected; in place of this they demanded the most rigorous logic.* Found wanting in logic were the simple statements met with in a course in analysis, such as:

"Consider the domain G bounded by the closed curve Γ."

What is a closed curve? Why is it the boundary of a domain? Into how many parts does a closed curve divide the plane, and which of these parts is being studied?

The mathematicians of the 18th century did not reply to these questions. They just drew an oval and thought that this was all that needed to be said. But no one believed in pictures in the 19th century. The question "what is a curve?" was only one of the vital questions facing analysts.

However, a long time went by before they succeeded in giving a comprehensive answer to this question.

A Curve Is the Path of a Moving Point

In order to arrive at a rigorous definition of curve it was necessary to move away from the concrete objects on which the formation of the mathematical concept was based: long, thin threads; light rays; long, narrow roads, etc. In all these cases the length is so much greater than the width that the latter can be neglected. After mathematical idealization we arrive at the notion of length without width.

---

* True, they frequently tended to throw out the baby with the bath; in the 20th century much of what was thrown out became once more part of science.

The first to try to give a rigorous definition of curve was the French mathematician Camille Jordan. He proceeded from the fact that the trajectory of the motion of a very small body may be represented by a long, narrow tube. As we diminish the size of the body, the tube becomes more and more narrow and in the limit becomes the trajectory of a moving point—a curve possessing no width. Jordan applied this image in his definition of curve. Namely, he called the trajectory of a moving point a curve. Here the point is to move in a continuous manner, not making any jumps.

Jordan's definition can be more exactly stated as follows: In order to determine the position of a moving point its coordinates must be given for each moment during the motion. Since the motion takes place over a finite time interval, we can assume without loss of generality that this interval is $[0, 1]$. In other words, the point begins to move at some moment of time taken as the origin of the observation and completes its motion after a certain unit of time has elapsed (a second, a minute, a year, etc). The coordinates of the moving point are given for each moment of time t during the passing of this interval. Thus, the coordinates of the point depend on the moment of time t, and so are functions of t. We shall denote these functions by $f(t)$ and $g(t)$:

$$x = f(t) \qquad y = g(t) \qquad (4.17)$$

The requirement that the point move continuously amounts to the requirement that the functions $f(t)$ and $g(t)$ be continuous at each point of the segment $[0, 1]$. Roughly speaking, a small change in t should produce only a small change in the functions $f(t)$ and $g(t)$. More precisely, if $t_1, \ldots, t_n, \ldots$ approaches a value t, $\lim_{n \to \infty} t_n = t$, then we have the equalities

$$\lim_{n \to \infty} f(t_n) = f(t) \qquad (4.18)$$

and

$$\lim_{n \to \infty} g(t_n) = g(t) \qquad (4.19)$$

Jordan's definition turned out to be rather a successful one. All the curves with which mathematicians had dealt up to this time turned out to be curves in Jordan's sense, or, as is said, *Jordan curves*. Take, for example, a circle of radius 1. The length of this circle is 2π. So the point must move with speed 2π in order to complete the circle in unit time. Thus, in time t it will move through the arc $2\pi t$.

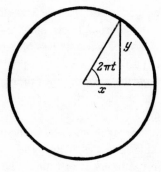

FIG. 33.

It is clear from Fig. 33 that its coordinates at time t must be given by the formulas

$$x = \cos 2\pi t$$
$$y = \sin 2\pi t \qquad (4.20)$$

These equations are called the parametric equations of the circle. And for the curve sketched in Fig. 34 (it is called the *astroid*) the parametric equations have the form:

$$x = \cos^3 2\pi t$$
$$y = \sin^3 2\pi t \tag{4.21}$$

Jordan curves may be made up of several different curves. Let us take as an example the contour of a semidisk,

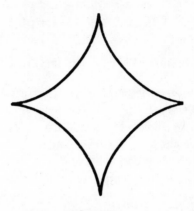

Fig. 34.

consisting of a semicircle of radius 1 and a diameter (Fig. 35). We let the moving point cover the semicircle in half the time and the diameter in the remaining half. We already know the expressions for the coordinates for motion along the circle. Under motion along the diameter, y remains

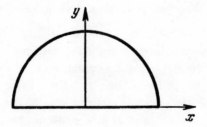

Fig. 35.

zero while x changes from -1 to 1. As a result we obtain the following parametric equations for the contour:

$$x = \begin{cases} \cos 2\pi t & \text{if} \quad 0 \leqslant t \leqslant \frac{1}{2} \\ 4t - 3 & \text{if} \quad \frac{1}{2} \leqslant t \leqslant 1 \end{cases} \tag{4.22}$$

$$y = \begin{cases} \sin 2\pi t & \text{if} \quad 0 \leqslant t \leqslant \frac{1}{2} \\ 0 & \text{if} \quad \frac{1}{2} \leqslant t \leqslant 1 \end{cases} \tag{4.23}$$

The Theorem Is Obvious, but the Proof Is Not

Employing his concept of curve, Jordan was successful in giving a precise meaning to the sentence from the analysis textbook that we spoke of earlier: "Let the closed curve Γ bound the domain G." A closed Jordan curve is a curve which passes through the point at $t = 1$ that was passed through at $t = 0$. The curve does not intersect itself as long as no two values of time t_1 and t_2 between 0 and 1 correspond to the same point on the curve.

Jordan proved the following theorem.

Theorem. *A closed Jordan curve Γ which does not intersect itself divides the plane into two parts. Two points contained in the same part can be connected by a broken line that does not intersect the curve Γ, but two points contained in different parts cannot be connected by such a broken line; any broken line connecting them must intersect the curve Γ* (Fig. 36).

This theorem seems completely obvious. Its proof, however, required very subtle arguments. Even when the curve Γ is the boundary of a polygon, the proof remains quite complicated. See if you can quickly decide whether or not the points A and B in Fig. 37 can be joined by a broken line which does not intersect the contour Γ.

The two parts into which a closed Jordan curve divides the plane are called the exterior and interior domains bounded by

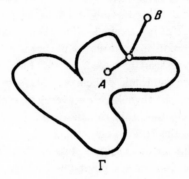

FIG. 36.

this curve. The concept of a domain bounded by a closed curve thus acquired an exact meaning.

FIG. 37.

A Curve Passing through All the Points of a Square

It appeared at first when Jordan gave his definition of curve that the goal had been achieved; a rigorous definition of the concept of curve was now available that did not depend on intuition. But it was quickly found out that this was not the case— Jordan's definition embraced not only what mathematicians usually called curves, but also geometric figures that no one would call curves. Mathematicians could somehow reconcile themselves to everywhere prickly curves, but no one had the heart to call a square a curve. But it did turn out that the square, the triangle, and the circle (not the perimeter of the figure, but in each case the figure itself with all its interior points) were curves in Jordan's sense. This was proved by the Italian mathematician Peano.

We already mentioned that Cantor set up a one-to-one correspondence between the points of the segment and those of the square, i.e., he showed that there are just as many points on the segment as are in the square. But his correspondence was not continuous. As the point moved along the segment, the corresponding point on the square did not crawl around like a beetle, but jumped around like a flea. Indeed, let us take the points

$$0.50000000\ldots \quad 0.499999990000000\ldots \quad (4.24)$$

on the segment. These points are quite close together. But the corresponding points on the square are far apart. For the point corresponding to the first of these is $(0.50000\ldots, 0.0000\ldots)$ situated on the bottom of the square, while the point corresponding to the second is $(0.4999000\ldots, 0.9999000\ldots)$ situated at the very top of the square. And if we increase the number of nines in the second point, thus bringing it closer to the first, the corresponding points on the square do not begin to approach one another.

Thus, Cantor's mapping of the segment onto the square, although one-to-one, was not continuous, and so did not give rise to a Jordan curve. Peano succeeded in setting up another mapping of the set of points of the segment onto the set of points of the square which sent neighboring points on the segment into neighboring points on the square. In other words, Peano was able to construct a curve (in Jordan's sense) which passed through all the points of the square!

Of course, we cannot draw Peano's curve, that is, unless we imitate an abstract painter and draw a black square. But, after all, the square is uniform, so we will not be able to see where the curve begins, where it ends and how it moves about the square. Therefore, we shall follow the example of the physicist Peppin, rather than that of the abstract painter, and sketch the position of the moving point using line segments. The shorter the intervals of time taken between separate "observations," the more accurately will the broken line thus obtained represent Peano's curve.

We shall first observe the position of the moving point every $\frac{1}{4}$ second. In other words, we observe its position at the beginning of the motion, at $\frac{1}{4}$ second after the beginning of the motion, at $\frac{1}{2}$ second after the beginning of the motion, at $\frac{3}{4}$ second and at the end of the motion. This gives us 5 points. Connecting them, we obtain the line ABCDE drawn in Fig. 38a.

Naturally, this line does not pass through all points of the curve. Now we reduce the interval of time between individual observations and observe the position of the point every 1/16 second. Now the curve twists more, the number of breaks increases and it takes the form sketched in Fig. 38b. If we observe the position of the moving point still

more often, we obtain the curve sketched in Fig. 38c. We
see that the curve fills the square more and more densely,
that it approaches more and more closely to each of its
points. In the limit, in which we would be constantly
observing the moving point, we would obtain a curve passing
through all points of the square without exception.

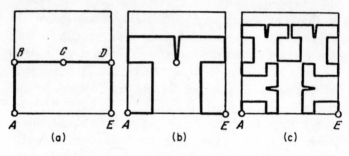

FIG. 38.

It should be noted that, while Peano has an advantage
over Cantor in that his curve is continuous, he falls short
in another respect. His curve no longer gave rise to a one-
to-one mapping of the segment onto the line; it passed
through some points of the square several times. It was
later proved that it is impossible to obtain a correspondence
that is both one-to-one and continuous: there does not
exist a Jordan curve passing through all the points of the
square exactly once!

Everything Had Come Unstrung

It is difficult to put into words the effect that Peano's
result had on the mathematical world. It seemed that
everything was in ruins, that all the basic mathematical
concepts had lost their meaning; the difference between

curve and surface, between surface and solid was no longer clear (the result showing the impossibility of a one-to-one continuous correspondence between the segment and the square was still unknown). The well-known French mathematician Henri Poincaré bitterly exclaimed:

"How was it possible that intuition could so deceive us?"

It soon became clear that Jordan's definition had, its faults. On the one hand it was too broad: Peano's curve fits this definition; but on the other hand it was too narrow: not all the figures that we intuitively want to call curves satisfied this definition. For example, the curve sketched in Fig. 27, p. 105 (the circle with the spiral wrapped around it), is not a Jordan curve. And still other, more deeply hidden, failings were detected in Jordan's definition—after all, this definition did not just deal with the curve, but also dealt with the rate at which the point generating the curve moved. For example, imagine a runner who runs the first half of the circle in $\frac{1}{4}$ minute, but then gets tired and takes $\frac{3}{4}$ minute to run the second half. Clearly, the parametric equations we get in this case are entirely different from (4.20).

And, after all, the point can traverse the circle in uncountably many ways, now speeding up, now slowing down. We thus obtain many different parametric equations for the same circle. It is very hard to guess that the equations

$$x = \frac{1 - t^2}{1 + t^2}$$

$$y = \frac{2t}{1 + t^2}$$

(4.25)

describe the same circle as the equations

$$x = \cos 2\pi t$$
$$y = \sin 2\pi t \qquad\qquad (4.26)$$

And it would be quite easy to be confused by more compli-cated curves. Take, for instance, the two-leafed rose. We can traverse this curve as in Fig. 39a or as in Fig. 39b. From Jordan's point of view we would get two entirely different curves; but, after all, how we traverse the curve does not matter—the curve remains the same.

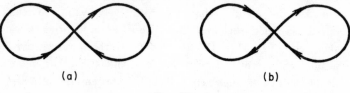

(a)   **(b)**

Fig. 39.

So the question was again raised: what is a curve and how does it differ from a surface? The answer was related to Cantor's general studies on geometric figures.

How to Make a Statue

Having founded the theory of sets, Cantor now turned his attention to the question: *what is a geometric figure*? The most general answer to this question would read: a geometric figure is any set of points in a space. If this set lies in the plane, then we obtain a plane geometric figure. But this answer would be too general—a "figure" in this sense would have no really interesting properties. The geometry of such figures would be almost devoid of theorems.

So it was first of all necessary to limit the class of sets to be studied, separating out those which had properties close to those of the ordinary geometric figures.

In order to separate out this class of figures we have to decide what it is that the ordinary figures such as the square, circle, line segment, astroid, etc, have in common. It turns out that we can construct all these figures by means of a single procedure.

It is said that when the famous sculptor Rodin was asked how he managed to make such remarkable statues, he replied: "I choose a block of marble and chop off whatever I do not need."

We can obtain any bounded plane geometric figure by this same method: we take a square which contains it and chop off whatever we do not need. Of course, we do not chop everything off at once, but proceed step by step, at each step removing circular pieces. Here we remove the interior of the circle, while its boundary, the circumference, is left in the figure.

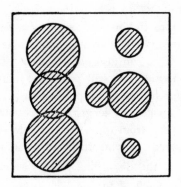

Fig. 40.

At first we might think that this procedure would only yield figures like those in Fig. 40. But the secret lies in the fact that we do not remove just one or two circles, but a countable set of circles. We can obtain any figure we like when we are allowed to cut out countably many circles. To do this we proceed as follows: take all circles both coordinates of whose centers and whose radius are rational numbers. The set of such circles is countable because of the Theorem 3.1 on p. 52. Next we remove from the plane all those circles of our set whose interiors contain no points of the geometric figure.

Clearly, only the geometric figure itself will remain after this operation, and the number of circles discarded is not more than countable.

However, we do not have to discard circles. Instead of them we could remove squares, rectangles, ellipses, observing only the restriction that the interior points are discarded while the boundary remains.

Continua

In addition to the ordinary geometric figures, it turns out that by means of removing a countable set of circles (or squares etc) we can also obtain other sets quite unlike the ordinary figures but still possessing many interesting properties. For instance, Sierpinski's carpet, of which we have already spoken at length, can be obtained in the following manner: from the square of side 1 discard small squares one by one, leaving their sides behind.

Moreover, by this discarding process we can also obtain "figures" not composed of a single piece. For example, if we remove "crosses",* as in Fig. 41, in the end we obtain a set not containing a single solid piece (said to be *completely disconnected*). Hence, we make the requirement that after

---

* Including terminal segments such as, for example, the segments *AB, CD, EF, GH*.

each discarding operation there must remain a set consisting of a single piece. Then after all the removals there will remain

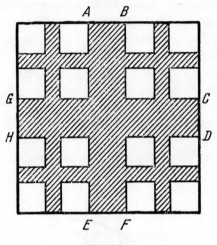

Fig. 41.

a set composed of a single piece (i.e., as mathematicians say, a *connected set*). The set obtained will also be bounded, i.e., it is entirely contained in some square.

A set F satisfying the following three conditions:

(1) the set F is obtained from a square by discarding a countable set of circles (or squares etc), leaving their boundaries,

(2) the set F is composed of a single piece (connected),

(3) the set F is bounded,

was said by Cantor to be a *continuum* (recall that the Latin word *continuum* means unbroken). The continuum turns out to be the most general set still possessing properties quite similar to those of ordinary geometric figures.

Cantor Curves

Now we are in a position to answer the question: what is a plane curve? Since plane curves must be geometric figures, it is clear that we must search for them among the continua. But the square and the circle are continua, and we certainly do not want to call these figures curves. Thus, we have to add on some other requirement which would eliminate such figures.

Note that both the circle and the square contain "solid" pieces of the plane. But a curve would not contain solid pieces of the plane; no matter how small a square we took, there would always be points on it not belonging to the curve (Fig. 42).

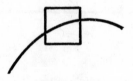

Fig. 42.

So here is the supplementary condition we need:

A plane curve in Cantor's sense is a continuum contained in the plane which does not fill any solid piece of the plane (i.e., in every square there are points not belonging to this curve).

For example, a segment, the boundary of a triangle, a circumference, a four-leafed rose are all curves. Sierpinski's carpet is also a curve; for in its construction we made holes in *all* the squares arising in the division, so that no solid piece of the plane is contained in it. Other Cantor curves ınclude the circle with the spiral wound around it and the saw-toothed curve of Fig. 43 together with the segment

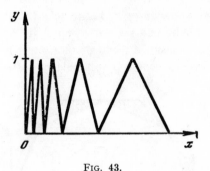

FIG. 43.

[0, 1] of the y axis. More generally, all those figures that seem to our intuitions to be curves are also curves in Cantor's sense, while any figure containing even one solid piece of the plane does not belong to the class of Cantor curves.

But even among Cantor curves are some whose properties are quite unlike those of ordinary curves. We shall now discuss some of these.

Can the Area of a Curve Be Different from Zero?

Of course, now that the reader has made the acquaintance of curves passing through all the points of a square, he will not be surprised by anything. But even so, can a curve have area? After all, Euclid did say that a curve is length without width. And how can we get area from something without width? In Cantor's definition of a curve, too, it says that the curve cannot contain any solid piece of the plane. Where will we find area in this case? But let us not rush to give a categorical reply.

Before we study the question, we must come to an understanding about the exact meaning of the words used. What is meant by the words *"a curve has zero area"* or *"a curve has nonzero area"*? Let us take the most ordinary curve—a straight line segment. Since its width is zero, we can place it inside a rectangle of arbitrarily small area; we only have to choose a rectangle of sufficiently small

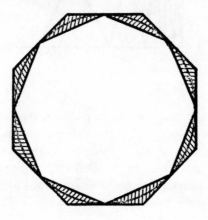

Fig. 44.

width. In exactly the same way we can put a circumference inside a polygon of arbitrarily small area. This can be done by inscribing a regular polygon with a very large number of sides and then circumscribing a similar polygon. The region included between the two polygons will have small area (the more sides our polygons have, the smaller the area), and the circle is entirely contained in this region (Fig. 44).

Now it is clear what is meant by the words *a curve has zero area*. They mean that no matter how small a positive number ε we take, we can find a polygonal domain which contains the curve and has an area less than ε. And if we cannot find such a domain, the area of the curve is not equal to zero.

In order to make the definition more clear we shall apply it to a more complicated curve than the simple segment or circle. Sierpinski's carpet represents, of course, a very complicated curve. Let us find its area. Recall first of all that the area of the whole square was 1. In the first step we discarded the central square of area 1/9. We thus got a polygonal domain of area 8/9. In the second step we discarded 8 squares each of which had area 1/81. This left a polygonal domain of area

$$\frac{8}{9} - \frac{8}{81} = \frac{64}{81} = \left(\frac{8}{9}\right)^2 \tag{4.27}$$

It is now clear that after the third step there will be left a polygonal domain of area $(8/9)^3$, then a domain with area $(8/9)^4$, etc. But if you take any proper fraction and raise it to higher and higher powers, the limit will be zero: if $0 < q < 1$, then

$$\lim_{n \to \infty} q^n = 0 \tag{4.28}$$

In particular, $\lim_{n \to \infty} (8/9)^n = 0$. But by definition of limit this means that for any $\varepsilon > 0$ we can find an n such that $(8/9)^n < \varepsilon$. This tells us that after n steps we get a polygonal domain of area less than ε. And this domain covers Sierpinski's carpet. As a consequence of this, the area of Sierpinski's carpet is zero.

This would seem to mark the complete triumph of Euclid's definition. Even such a complicated curve as Sierpinski's carpet has area zero. But it would be premature to celebrate the triumph now. After all, no one forced us to discard such large pieces. Let us proceed more economically and divide the square into 25 equal parts, rather than into 9 (i.e., we divide each side into 5 parts). We discard the central square, whose area is, obviously, 1/25. Probably now the reader will want to divide each of the remaining 24 small squares into 25 parts and discard the central part. But this would again be uneconomical. Instead of this we take the segments bounding the discarded square and continue them until they intersect with the sides of the large square. This gives us 4 squares (in the corners) and 4 rectangles.

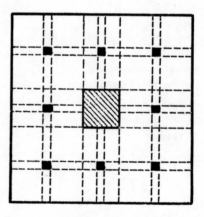

FIG. 45.

In each square and each rectangle we construct crosses with cross-pieces of width 1/25, discarding the central part of the cross (Fig. 45). Since the area of the central part is 1/625, the area of all the squares discarded in the second step is 8/625. Following this procedure, in the third step we discard 64 small squares of total area $64/25^3 = 64/15,625$

etc. The area of the discarded squares will now be given by the geometric progression

$$\frac{1}{25} + \frac{8}{25^2} + \frac{64}{25^3} + \cdots \qquad (4.29)$$

with multiplier 8/25. The sum of this progression is only 1/17. But what does this mean? This means that at each step an area of not less than 16/17 falls to the share of what is not discarded. So no polygonal domain of area less than 16/17 can possibly cover what is left. Now, this remainder, just as in the case of Sierpinski's carpet, is a curve (in Cantor's sense)—in constructing it we made a hole in every square and rectangle and not a single solid rectangle or square was left behind.

As a result, therefore, a curve in Cantor's sense can have nonzero area!

Domains without Area

Even so, the example we analyzed is not too convincing: the curve we obtained intersects itself everywhere and does not bound any domain. So the question arises: can a "good" curve that does not intersect itself, have nonzero area? It happens that it can!

We can construct such a curve by changing a little the construction carried out before. We first construct a set in which you not only cannot find a solid piece of square, but not even a solid piece of curve, and the area of this set will not be zero. To do this we have to discard whole crosses rather than central squares, as is shown in Fig. 46. Here we select the dimensions of the crosses so that the area of the first discarded cross will be 8/25, the area of all crosses discarded in the second step will be $64/625 = (8/25)^2$, the area of those discarded in the third step $(8/25)^3$ etc. Then

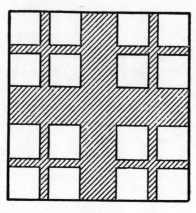

Fig. 46.

the total area of the discarded crosses will equal the sum of the geometric progression

$$\frac{8}{25} + \left(\frac{8}{25}\right)^2 + \left(\frac{8}{25}\right)^3 + \cdots \qquad (4.30)$$

i.e., $8/17$. But this is less than half the area of the original square. This means that an area of $9/17$ of the original square is left to the part remaining. Now in constructing the set we discarded whole crosses, ruthlessly tearing up the square. No two points of the set remaining can be connected by a curve, not even a curve in Cantor's sense; every connection between its points has been broken. As mathematicians would say, the remainder is a completely disconnected set. And still the area of this set, not containing a single piece of the plane nor an arc of a curve, is different from zero; you cannot cover this set with a polygonal domain of area less than 9/17.

Now it is easy to construct an example of a closed curve that does not intersect itself and has nonzero area. To do this we need only connect the points we already have just as we drew a curve through all the points of the square. And because we discarded whole crosses at each step, our curve will not intersect itself (in this it differs from Peano's curve). But since it passes through all points of the set, whose area must be at least 9/17, the area of the curve obtained must be at least 9/17.

It is also no trouble now to construct a domain without area. For this we need only connect two points A and B of our curve with some kind of curve, perhaps a semicircle. Then we obtain a curve which bounds some domain G. And what is its area? The answer depends on whether or not we include the boundary with the domain—after all, the boundary itself has an area of at least 9/17. Clearly, our domain has no area in the ordinary sense of the word. In mathematics such domains not having area in the usual sense are called *nonquadratisable*.

Some Surprising Examples

It is probable that after the appearance of Peano's curve mathematicians were sure that they had already seen all the "miracles" that take place in the world of unusual functions and curves. But then their geometrical intuition let them down again. The properties of Cantor curves are so different from those of ordinary curves that we will do well to recount the following story.

At the beginning of the 20th century the well-known mathematician Schoenflies published a series of works in

which he discussed various properties of curves, the boundaries of domains, etc.   In these articles Schoenflies often
relied on "geometric obviousness."   But a few years later,
in 1910, there appeared a short (only 12 pages) article by
the young Dutch mathematician Brouwer.   It contained
several surprising examples, in consequence of which one
of Schoenflies' results was simply false and others, although
correct, were not rigorously proved.   In truth, some naughty
pranks were played on Schoenflies' "geometrically obvious"!

In order to show which "obvious" statements turned
out to be false we shall present some of Brouwer's examples
(we shall actually use some later simplifications).

Brouwer constructed a bounded domain whose border
was not a continuum.   In order to do this he took a "bottle"
and began to extend its neck, winding it around a circle
(Fig. 47).

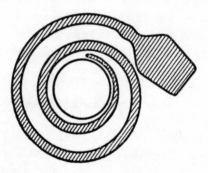

F IG.   47.

As a result he obtained a domain bounded by two spirals
and the "bottle."   But this boundary is not a continuum;
for in order to obtain a continuum we would have to add
in the circle around which the spirals are wound.

Domains and Boundaries

Since we have been discussing boundaries and domains, let us pause here to make these concepts more precise. After all, it turned out that Jordan's definition of a curve was not too successful, so that we need to give a new definition for a domain.

We shall call an *open set* in the plane, any set consisting of a sum of circles with their boundaries removed. In particular, the complement of any plane continuum is an open set in the plane. All the usual planar domains (the interiors of a circle, a square, a triangle, etc) are open sets (in the plane). In addition, these sets are connected; any two of their points can be joined by a broken line which does not leave the domain. These are also the properties that define a planar domain.

A planar domain is a connected set of points of the plane composed of a sum of circles with their boundaries removed.

Here the number of circles can be arbitrary. However, we can show that any domain can be composed from a countable set of circles.

A circle with its boundary removed is called a *neighborhood* of its center *a*. Of course, each point has infinitely many neighborhoods.

A point *a* in the plane is called a *boundary point* of domain *G* if every neighborhood of point *a* contains points of domain *G* as well as points not belonging to *G* (Fig. 48).

Open sets, domains and boundary points of domains in space are defined in exactly the same way. The difference consists in choosing spheres with their boundaries removed in place of circles with their boundaries removed.

In addition to the concept of neighborhood of a point (in the plane or in space) we shall need the concept of *relative neighborhood of a point* belonging to some set A. That is what we call the set of points of a neighborhood that belong to set A, i.e., the intersection of an ordinary neighborhood of the point with just the set A. For example, if A is the

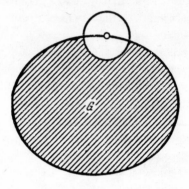

Fig. 48.

curve drawn in Fig. 49 and G is the neighborhood of the point A, then the relative neighborhood of this point is the arc of the curve between points b and c. If the set A consists of several points, then each of its points is a relative neighborhood of itself. In order to see

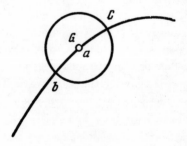

Fig. 49.

this, simply take an ordinary neighborhood of the point which does not contain any of the remaining points of the set (Fig. 50).

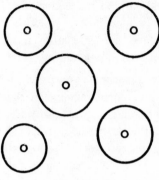

Fig. 50.

The Great Irrigation Project

We shall now talk about a second, even more surprising example of Brouwer. Let us draw the map of some country and the countries contiguous to it. Almost every point of the boundary of this country belongs to two and only two countries: the given one and one of its neighbors. On the map there are some points where three countries come together (Fig. 51). Three border guards stand at such

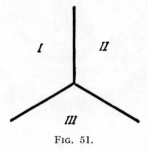

Fig. 51.

points. But there is only a finite number of such places on
the map. And it seems quite obvious that such points
could not occupy the whole boundary of a country, i.e.,
that there could not be three domains (three countries)
sharing the same boundary. In other words, it seems
obvious that three border guards from three different
countries will not be standing at every point of the boundary.

But Brouwer constructed three such domains. In order
to understand his example, imagine an island in the ocean on
which there are two lakes with fresh water. Only, one lake
is cold and the other is warm. Now we shall carry out the
following irrigation project. During the first day we
construct canals leading from the ocean and from both
lakes in such a way that each canal is "blind" (i.e., is only

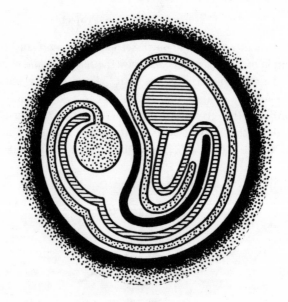

Fig. 52.

a creek of the corresponding reservoir), that the canals
nowhere touch one another and so that, when we have
finished, each point of dry land is at a distance of less than
1 kilometer from sea water and from the water of both
lakes (Fig. 52).

During the following half day we extend these canals
in such a way that they remain "blind" as before and do
not touch one another, and so that now the distance from
any point of dry land to any of the three canals is less than
$\frac{1}{2}$ kilometer. In doing this, of course, the canals have to
be made narrower than they were before. In the following
quarter day we carry on, arranging matters so that each
point of dry land is less than $\frac{1}{4}$ kilometer from any canal,
etc. As we continue the process, the canals become ever
more winding and narrower. After two days' work the entire
island will be permeated by these three canals and converted
into a Cantor curve. No matter what point of the curve
we stand on, we can scoop up, according to our whim, salt
water or warm or cold fresh water. And things are so
arranged that the waters do not mix with one another. If
we replaced the ocean and lakes by three countries, we would
obtain the unusual map we spoke of at the beginning—three
border guards, one from each country, could be placed at
each point of the boundary.

A "Nondissertable" Subject

We already said that Cantor's definition had one fault—
it was not at all suitable for curves in space. But then what
is a surface in space? No one knew. This problem—to
determine what curves and surfaces in space are—was put
in the summer of 1921 to his twentythree year old student
Pavel Samuelovich Urysohn by the venerable Professor

Dmitri Fedorovich Yegorov of Moscow University (it is evident that he thought a lot about the mathematical significance of the problem or, as is sometimes said today, of the "dissertability" of the subject—this problem was one of the hardest!)

Urysohn quickly comprehended that Yegorov's problem was only a special case of a much more general problem: what is the dimension of a geometric figure, i.e., what are the characteristics of the figure which cause us to say that a segment or circumference has dimension 1, a square has dimension 2, and a cube or sphere has dimension 3? Here is what is remembered about this period in the life of P. S. Urysohn by his closest friend, a young doctoral candidate in those days and now an academician, the honorary president of the Moscow Mathematical Society, Pavel Sergeevich Aleksandrov: "...the whole summer of 1921 was spent in trying to find an 'up-to-date' definition (of dimension); P. S. shifted his interest from one variant to another, constantly setting up examples showing why this or that variant had to be eliminated. He spent two months totally absorbed in his meditations. At last, one morning near the end of August, P. S. awoke with his now well-known inductive definition of dimension in its final form.... That very morning, while we were bathing in the Klyaz'ma, P. S. Urysohn told me about his definition of dimension and there, during the conversation that extended over several hours, outlined a plan for a complete theory of dimension composed of a series of theorems, which were then hypotheses that he did not yet know how to go about proving and which were later proved one after another in the months that followed. I never again either participated in or witnessed a mathematical conversation composed of such a dense flow of new ideas as the conversation of that

August morning. The whole program outlined then was realized during the winter of 1921/22; by the spring of 1922 the whole theory of dimension was ready..."

The basic idea of Urysohn's definition of dimension consisted of the following. Two or perhaps several points usually suffice for separating a portion of a curve from the remainder (the part of the four-leafed rose of Fig. 53 con-

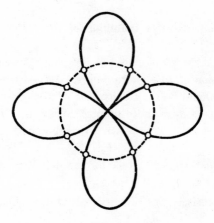

FIG. 53.

taining the center can be separated from the rest of the curve by using eight points). But it is already impossible to separate a part of a surface from the remainder by removing several points—for this you have to take a complete curve—no matter how many points you take on the surface, it is always possible to go around them. In the same way a surface is needed to separate a part of three-dimensional space from the rest of the space.

All this still had to be made more precise; for some curves an infinite set of points had to be taken in order to separate off some part, but the totality of these points still did not form a curve. Urysohn succeeded in giving a precise formulation to all the definitions required. In a way his definitions were reminiscent of those of Euclid (the ends of a curve are points, the ends of a surface are curves). But this resemblance is something like the one between the hollowed-out tree trunk of primitive man and a modern liner.

The Inductive Definition of Dimension

Let us now discuss more precisely how Urysohn defined the dimension of a geometric figure. A typical zero-dimensional set would be a set consisting of a single point or, in the worst case, of a finite number of points. But in such a set each point has a relative neighborhood with empty boundary—the point itself (see Fig. 50). This was the property that Urysohn took for his definition of a set of dimension zero.

More precisely, his definition went like this:

A set F has dimension zero, if each of its points has an arbitrarily small relative neighborhood with empty boundary.

In most cases it is possible to establish that a set has dimension zero by selecting for each point an arbitrarily small ordinary neighborhood whose boundary contains no point of the set F (then the boundary of the relative neighborhood is sure to be empty). But there are zero-dimensional sets situated in three-dimensional space for whose points such ordinary neighborhoods are not available.

The words "arbitrarily small" are inserted in the definition for the following reason. If these were not there, then we could, for instance, find a circle big enough to hold an entire square within it and so that no point of the square would lie on the boundary of the circle. So if these words were not in the definition, we would find that the dimension of a square is zero, not two as it really is.

In addition to finite sets, many infinite sets have dimension zero. For example, take the set of points on the x axis with coordinates $0, 1, \frac{1}{2}, \frac{1}{3}, \ldots, 1/n, \ldots$. It is clear that any point of this set has an arbitrarily small neighborhood that does not contain any points of this set. Only the case of the point 0 might cause some doubts. But if we take a neighborhood of radius α, where α is an irrational number, then no point of the set will occur on the boundary of this neighborhood.

The set Q of points on a line with rational coordinates is also zero-dimensional. To convince yourself of this, simply take an interval of irrational length centered at point a of Q as the neighborhood of point a. Cantor's set also has dimension zero (see p. 97) as does the set obtained by discarding crosses from the square (see p. 126) and many other sets.

We can similarly construct zero-dimensional sets in space as well as in the plane (in doing so, of course, we take neighborhoods of points to be neighborhoods in space).

After defining sets of dimension zero, Urysohn went on to one-dimensional sets, i.e., to curves. Here there are no longer small neighborhoods with empty boundaries (see Fig. 53). However, in the case of ordinary curves the boundary of the neighborhood only intersects the curve in a few points. But a set composed of a finite number of points has dimension zero. Generalizing this situation, Urysohn defined a set of dimension one in the following way.

A set F has *dimension one*, if it is not zero-dimensional and each of its points has an arbitrarily small neighborhood whose boundary intersects the set F in a zero-dimensional set.

It turned out that not only all the ordinary curves (circle, line segment, ellipse, etc) but also all Cantor curves have dimension *one* in Urysohn's sense. Thus, it now became possible to define the notion of a curve in space as well as in the plane.

A curve is a continuum of dimension one.

And it was also clear how to define surface, three-dimensional solid and, in general, a set of any dimension. Since the definition proceeds by numerical order, first defining a set of dimension 0, then a set of dimension 1, then of dimension 2, etc, Urysohn's definition of dimension is called *inductive*.

The Article Is to Be Printed, not Reviewed!

Urysohn proved many very interesting theorems relating to the notion of dimension that he introduced. But he was unable to find a way to prove one very important theorem; he could not prove that an ordinary cube has dimension 3. After prolonged effort he found a remarkable way out of the difficulty, conceiving a new definition of dimension in the process. We shall not discuss this definition in detail, but shall simply illustrate it on very simple figures.

If we take a segment or a circle, we can divide it into arbitrarily small pieces in such a way that each point belongs to at most two pieces (Fig. 54). Here we take the pieces together with their boundaries (i.e., their endpoints). But a square cannot be divided this way. It seems at first glance that if we divide a square into pieces, there will always be

points belonging to four pieces (Fig. 55a). But if we place
the pieces the way they lay bricks in construction work,
we can do it in such a way that each point belongs to at

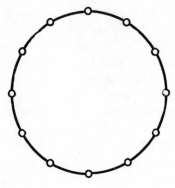

FIG. 54.

most three different pieces (Fig. 55b). In the same way,
we can divide up the cube into small parallelopipeds in such
a way that each point belongs to at most four parallelopipeds.

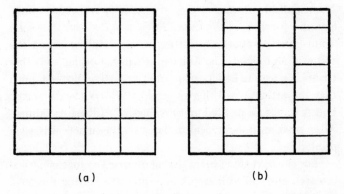

(a)   (b)

FIG. 55.

This is the property that Urysohn took for his new definition of dimension. A figure is said to have dimension n,
if it can be divided into arbitrarily small closed parts in
such a way that no point belongs to $n + 2$ different parts,
but for a sufficiently fine subdivision there will be points
belonging to $n + 1$ different parts.

The parts into which the figure is divided are not
completely arbitrary; their complements must be open sets
(such parts are called closed).

Employing this definition of dimension, Urysohn proved
that the dimension of the square is 2, that the dimension
of the cube is 3, etc. And he then proved that this definition
is equivalent to the one given first.

Urysohn's theory of dimension made a great impression
on the mathematical world. This is vividly expressed by
the following episode. During a trip abroad Urysohn gave
a report on his results at Göttingen. Before the rise of the
Fascists to power the University of Göttingen was one of
the leading mathematical centers. After the report the
head of the Göttingen school of mathematics, David Hilbert,
said that the results should be published in the journal
Mathematische Annalen —one of the most respected mathematical journals of the time. A few months later, Urysohn
again gave a report at Göttingen, and Hilbert asked the
editor of Mathematische Annalen, Richard Courant, whether
Urysohn's article had been printed yet. The latter replied
that the article was being reviewed. "But I clearly stated
that it was to be printed, not reviewed!" Hilbert exclaimed.
After such an unequivocal declaration the article was soon
printed.

For the next three years Urysohn carried on mathematical
research unequalled in depth and intensity (during this time
he published several dozen articles). A tragic accident

abruptly ended his life—he drowned August 17, 1924 while swimming during a storm in the Bay of Biscay. He completed his last mathematical article the day before his death.

After Urysohn's death there still remained numerous rough drafts and outlines of unpublished results. His closest friend (and co-author of his many articles) Pavel Sergeevich Aleksandrov interrupted his own studies for a time and prepared these articles for publication, thus making these additional results of Urysohn available to all mathematicians. The theory of dimension at present constitutes an important chapter of mathematics.

Conclusion

Infinite sets possess remarkable properties. In studying these properties mathematicians were led to continually perfect their reasoning and to further develop mathematical logic. It was thought for a long time that the theory of sets and mathematical logic were abstract sciences having no practical application. But when electronic computers were invented, it turned out that their programming was based on mathematical logic, and many investigations previously thought to be remote from practical affairs acquired the greatest practical significance (this often happens in the history of science—even at the beginning of the 1930's a book could still be published saying: "Uranium has no practical uses.")

At present the theory of sets is fundamental for such areas of mathematics as functional analysis, topology, general algebra, etc. Profound studies are still being made in the theory of sets itself. These studies relate to the very foundations of mathematics. In these studies it has become clear that the "naive" approach to the concept of set that we took in this book is far from adequate. It has become necessary to axiomatize the concept of set. However, these investigations lie far outside the scope envisioned in the planning of this book.

Exercises and Examples

1. Set A consists of the integers divisible by 4, set B consists of the integers divisible by 10, and set C consists of the integers divisible by 75. What numbers are in the set ABC?

2. A library has books from various fields of science and art. Let A denote the set of all books in the library and let B denote the set of all mathematical books (not just the ones in the library). Characterize the set $A - B$.

3. Employing the rules of the algebra of logic, simplify the expression

$$(A + B + C)(A + B) - [A + (B - C)]A$$

4. What cardinal number is given by $2^{\aleph_0 c} + \aleph_0 c$.

5. Set up a one-to-one correspondence between the points of the segment $[0, 1]$ and the points of the interval $(0, 1)$ (i.e., the segment with its endpoints 0 and 1 removed).

6. Prove that the set of points in the plane with both coordinates rational is countable.

7. Prove that you cannot find in the plane more than a countable set of mutually nonintersecting circular discs.

8. Find in the plane a continuum of mutually nonintersecting circular circumferences.

9. Prove that you cannot find more than a countable set of mutually nonintersecting figure eights in the plane.

10. Show that it is not possible to find in the plane a larger than countable set of curves having the form of the letter *T*.

11. Suppose that we have enumerated all the rational points of the segment [0, 1]. We obtain a sequence of points $r_1, r_2, \ldots, r_n, \ldots$. We construct a neighborhood centered at r_1 with radius 1/10, a neighborhood centered at r_2 with radius 1/20, a neighborhood centered at r_3 with radius 1/40, etc. We sum up all the neighborhoods obtained. Will the set *M* thus obtained coincide with the entire segment?

12. Let the rational points be enumerated as in (3.9), p. 50. Produce an example of a point not found in set *M* of exercise 11.

13. We call the set of all sequences of real numbers $(x_1, \ldots, x_n, \ldots)$ such that $0 \leqslant x_n \leqslant 1$ the cube of countable dimension. Show that the set of points in this cube has the cardinality of the continuum.

14. Construct a continuous function that has infinitely many maxima and minima on each segment.

15. The set *M* consists of the points of the segment [0, 1] which have decimal representations in which neither of the digits 3 and 8 occur. Describe a procedure for obtaining this set by discarding intervals from the segment.

16. Do the same for points whose decimal expansions do not contain the combination 38 (in the given order).

17. A point *a* is called the limit point of a set *M*, if in each of its neighborhoods there are an infinite number of points of this set. Show that all the limit points of Cantor's set (see p. 97) already belong to the set. Show conversely that all points of Cantor's set are limit points of the set. Do the same for the sets of exercises 15 and 16.

18. Show that each point of the segment $[0, 1]$ is a limit
for the set of all rational numbers such that $0 \leqslant r \leqslant 1$.

19. Does the set of integers have any limit points?

20. Prove that the complement of any open set in the plane
contains all its limit points.

21. Prove that if a set contains all its limit points, its
complement is an open set.

CONSTITUTIONAL
AMENDMENTS
BEYOND THE BILL OF RIGHTS

Amendment XV
Race and the Right
to Vote

Other Books of Related Interest

Opposing Viewpoints Series

Civil Liberties

Feminism

Race Relations

Work

Working Women

Current Controversies Series

Civil Liberties

Extremist Groups

Feminism

Human Rights

CONSTITUTIONAL
AMENDMENTS
BEYOND THE BILL OF RIGHTS

Amendment XV
Race and the Right
to Vote

Jeff Hay, **Book Editor**

GREENHAVEN PRESS
A part of Gale, Cengage Learning

GALE
CENGAGE Learning·

Detroit • New York • San Francisco • New Haven, Conn • Waterville, Maine • London

Christine Nasso, *Publisher*
Elizabeth Des Chenes, *Managing Editor*

© 2009 Greenhaven Press, a part of Gale, Cengage Learning.

Gale and Greenhaven Press are registered trademarks used herein under license.

For more information, contact:
Greenhaven Press
27500 Drake Rd.
Farmington Hills, MI 48331-3535
Or you can visit our Internet site at gale.cengage.com

Articles in Greenhaven Press anthologies are often edited for length to meet page requirements. In addition, original titles of these works are changed to clearly present the main thesis and to explicitly indicate the author's opinion. Every effort is made to ensure that Greenhaven Press accurately reflects the original intent of the authors. Every effort has been made to trace the owners of copyrighted material.

Cover photograph © Flip Schulke/Corbis.

LIBRARY OF CONGRESS CATALOGING-IN-PUBLICATION DATA

Amendment XV : race and the right to vote / Jeff Hay, book editor.
    p. cm. -- (Constitutional amendments: beyond the Bill of Rights)
    Includes bibliographical references and index.
    ISBN 978-0-7377-4327-2 (hardcover)
    1. United States. Constitution. 15th Amendment. 2. African Americans--Suffrage--History. 3. Suffrage--United States. I. I. Hay, Jeff.
    KF4893.A96 2009
    342.73'072--dc22

                            2009004704

Printed in the United States of America
1 2 3 4 5 6 7 13 12 11 10 09

Contents

Chapter 1: Historical Background on the Fifteenth Amendment

Chapter 2: Challenging and Affirming the Fifteenth Amendment

Chapter 3: Ensuring Voting Rights in Contemporary America

Appendices

Race and the Right to Vote

> "Today's Constitution is a realistic document of freedom only because of several corrective amendments. Those amendments speak to a sense of decency and fairness."
>
> Thurgood Marshall

While the U.S. Constitution forms the backbone of American democracy, the amendments make the Constitution a living, ever-evolving document. Interpretation and analysis of the Constitution inform lively debate in every branch of government, as well as among students, scholars, and all other citizens, and views on various articles of the Constitution have changed over the generations. Formally altering the Constitution, however, can happen only through the amendment process. The Greenhaven Press series The Bill of Rights examines the first ten amendments to the Constitution. Constitutional Amendments: Beyond the Bill of Rights continues the exploration, addressing key amendments ratified since 1791.

The process of amending the Constitution is painstaking. While other options are available, the method used for nearly every amendment begins with a congressional bill that must pass both the Senate and the House of Representatives by a two-thirds majority. Then the amendment must be ratified by three-quarters of the states. Many amendments have been proposed since the Bill of Rights was adopted in 1791, but only seventeen have been ratified.

It may be difficult to imagine a United States where women and African Americans are prohibited from voting, where the federal government allows one human being to enslave another, or where some citizens are denied equal protection under the law. While many of our most fundamental liberties are protected by the Bill of Rights, the amendments that followed have significantly broadened and enhanced the rights of American citizens. Such rights may be taken for granted today, but when the amendments were ratified, many were considered groundbreaking and proved to be explosively controversial.

Each volume in Constitutional Amendments provides an in-depth exploration of an amendment and its impact through primary and secondary sources, both historical and contemporary. Primary sources include landmark Supreme Court rulings, speeches by prominent experts, and newspaper editorials. Secondary sources include historical analyses, law journal articles, book excerpts, and magazine articles. Each volume first presents the historical background of the amendment, creating a colorful picture of the circumstances surrounding the amendment's passage: the campaigns to sway public opinion, the congressional debates, and the struggle for ratification. Next, each volume examines the ways the court system has been used to test the validity of the amendment and addresses the ramifications of the amendment's passage. The final chapter of each volume presents viewpoints that explore current controversies and debates relating to ways in which the amendment affects our everyday lives.

Numerous features are included in each Constitutional Amendments volume:

- An originally written introduction presents a concise yet thorough overview of the amendment.

- A time line provides historical context by describing key events, organizations, and people relating to the ratification of the amendment, subsequent court cases, and the impact of the amendment.

- An annotated table of contents offers an at-a-glance summary of each primary and secondary source essay included in the volume.

- The complete text of the amendment, followed by a "plain English" explanation, brings the amendment into clear focus for students and other readers.

- Graphs, charts, tables, and maps enhance the text.

- A list of all twenty-seven Constitutional Amendments offers quick reference.

- An annotated list of court cases relevant to the amendment broadens the reader's understanding of the judiciary's role in interpreting the Constitution.

- A bibliography of books, periodicals, and Web sites aids readers in further research.

- A detailed subject index allows readers to quickly find the information they need.

With the aid of this series, students and other researchers will become better informed of their rights and responsibilities as American citizens. Constitutional Amendments: Beyond the Bill of Rights examines the roots of American democracy, bringing to life the ways the Constitution has evolved and how it has impacted this nation's history.

Amendment Text and Explanation

The Fifteenth Amendment to the United States Constitution

Passed by Congress February 26, 1869. Ratified February 3, 1870.

Section 1. The right of citizens of the United States to vote shall not be denied or abridged by the United States or by any State on account of race, color, or previous condition of servitude—

Section 2. The Congress shall have the power to enforce this article by appropriate legislation.

Explanation

The Fifteenth Amendment is among the shortest and most straightforward of all Constitutional Amendments. By ensuring that African Americans could not have their ability to vote interfered with, and by indeed guaranteeing the right to vote for all, it built upon the Thirteenth Amendment, which banned slavery in the United States, and the Fourteenth Amendment, which assured citizenship rights to former slaves as well as all African Americans and members of other non-white groups.

In the American tradition, the right to vote is an essential right of citizenship. Section 1 of the Fifteenth Amendment asserts that, as long as one is a U.S. citizen, one maintains that right. He (no woman had the right to vote as of the ratification of the Amendment in 1870) will have the ability to vote in both national elections as well as elections held in any of the individual states. The Amendment makes it clear that "race, color, or previous condition of servitude" will not be barriers to the right to vote at either level.

By "previous condition of servitude," the framers of the Fifteenth Amendment meant those people who had been slaves up until President Abraham Lincoln's Emancipation Proclamation of 1863, which ended slavery in the Union, or Northern states, and the Thirteenth Amendment of 1865, which banned slavery in the defeated Confederate, or Southern states. Since slaves were now free U.S. citizens, they must be given the right to vote.

While the intent of the Fifteenth Amendment was to protect the voting rights of African Americans, its framers broadened the language to assert that "race" [and] "color" would not be bars to voting rights, provided the voters were U.S. citizens. Therefore the Fifteenth Amendment's guarantees would apply not only to African Americans, but to other groups who might potentially find their voting rights challenged. These might include Americans of Asian background, Native Americans, or even Jews.

Section 1 of the Fifteenth Amendment emphasizes that a citizen's right to vote will not be "denied or abridged." Such hindrances to voting were, and are, a particular challenge in maintaining voting rights because voting procedures are set by individual states rather than by the federal government. The states maintain this right according to the original United States Constitution. In the time period when the Fifteenth Amendment was proposed, a number of Southern states enacted local laws or procedures that limited the ability of African Americans to vote. Such "denials" or "abridgements" included techniques like requiring literacy tests and charging poll taxes. The writers of the amendment wanted to be clear that these local laws would be overturned and that any future attempt to enact measures like them would be illegal. The Constitution and its Amendments in general take precedence over the laws of the states.

Section 2 of the Fifteenth Amendment asserts that the national Congress will maintain the ability to make sure that an

American citizen's voting rights are not limited or taken away. It will do so, when necessary, through it's lawmaking powers.

Introduction

Although one might imagine the issue to be fairly straight-forward in a democratic republic, the question of who has the right to vote in the United States has been the source of a great deal of controversy since the original U.S. Constitution was ratified in 1789. Much of this controversy has been based in the unique nature of the country, which combines diverse individual states into a single federation. While most Americans have agreed that any citizen should maintain the ability to cast ballots, both the federal government and the governments of individual states have had different standards for citizenship at different times. In addition, one of the rights closely held by the states is the right to set and establish procedures for elections and for registering and confirming voters. In fact the U.S. Constitution, prior to the ratification of the Fifteenth Amendment in 1870, said little about voting rights, leaving such matters to the individual states.

In the early years of the American union, most states restricted voting to adult men who possessed a certain amount of wealth or property. Ironically, this included a few examples of free African Americans, even in Southern states. Some states also, at first, in their own constitutions excluded as voters men who were not followers of one of the Protestant branches of Christianity, although these rules were rendered null and void by Article Six of the federal constitution, which established that no "religious test" could be used for voters. Still, the state of Maryland only granted voting rights to Jewish people in 1828. States continued to change their rules in the early and middle decades of the 1800s until by 1860, in most states, all adult white men could vote. Meanwhile, in most of the states where in earlier periods free African Americans could vote, those rights were later denied, and none of America's large population of slaves had any right to vote at all.

According to the United States census of 1860, taken the year before the Civil War began, there were approximately 4 million slaves in the country. Virtually all of them were of African origin, the descendants of people kidnapped in Africa and brought forcibly to America or to other nations of the Western Hemisphere. Although in earlier periods slaves could be found in all states, by the time of the Civil War the vast majority of them lived in the South. Those states, with large plantations of cotton, tobacco, and other agricultural commodities at the center of their economic life, had come to rely on slave labor. In addition to fieldwork on plantations, Southern slaves were also commonly used as household workers, and they could even be found from time to time in the houses and shops and on the farms of free African Americans. Across the Southern states slaves made up as much as one-third of the total population.

The issue of slavery was inevitably tied to the issue of states' rights. Northern states had abolished slavery by 1860, with Massachusetts being the first to do so in 1780, and many people living in the North continued to hold that slavery was a moral evil in the years leading up to 1860. Southerners, however, considered slavery essential to their economic well-being, and commonly argued that residents of Northern states had no right to interfere in their affairs. As the United States expanded westward, controversies arose over whether new states should be slaveholding ones, most notably in the "Bleeding Kansas" of the 1850s, where widespread public violence broke out over the issue. Adding further fuel to the fire was the sense that a rough balance of slave versus free states should be maintained in the federal government so that the interests of both could be adequately represented.

In 1860 Abraham Lincoln was elected president. He was a member of the Republican Party, a new, liberal party, outspoken members of which wanted to ban slavery across the country. Lincoln's victory also came with his name missing from the ballot in ten Southern states, where residents therefore considered his presidency less than fully legitimate. Southerners feared not only that Republicans would end slavery, but that the large numbers of newly freed slaves in the Southern states would overturn an established economic and social order. Beginning with South Carolina in April 1861, eleven Southern states seceded from the Union and formed their own nation, the Confederate States of America. Lincoln, for his part, pledged to preserve the Union. The result was the Civil War of 1861–1865, which ended in a Union victory at the cost of some six hundred thousand lives.

In 1863 Lincoln issued a proclamation of emancipation, which declared an end to slavery in the Confederate states and, effectively, in any remaining state allied with the Union. The 1865 victory over the Confederacy allowed the proclamation to be put into force, and in the Thirteenth Amendment to the United States Constitution, ratified in 1865, guaranteed that slavery would no longer exist in the country.

The end of the war and the end of slavery, however, did not provide any immediate calm in the nation. Until the late 1870s the United States remained in a period known commonly as Reconstruction. Among the major concerns of the Reconstruction era were the citizenship status and legal rights of some 4 million newly freed slaves, or freedmen as they were commonly known.

The Fourteenth Amendment to the U.S. Constitution addressed some of these problems. Ratified in 1868, it guaranteed citizenship rights to freed slaves and their descendants, rights which had been explicitly denied them in the Supreme Court's Dred Scott decision in 1857. It also required the states to grant equal protection to freedmen, or, in other words, to extend them the same legal rights that white Americans enjoyed. But the Fourteenth Amendment did nothing to explicitly guarantee to freedmen the right to vote, one of the most basic features of citizenship in a republic.

In the months following the Civil War, the former slave states enacted so-called Black Codes to limit the rights and freedoms of former slaves. Among the most vivid of these were rules denying them the right to vote. White leaders in these states feared that by allowing freedmen the right to vote their own power in national government would be diluted, since former slaves made up a large percentage of the populations in those states. In the antislavery North, however, leaders commonly saw the Black Codes as a newer, more subtle form of slavery. Opposition to them helped sweep into power the so-called Radical Republicans, who dominated Congress until the end of the 1860s. These Radical Republicans increased national control over the former slave states and required them to hold new elections in which freedmen could vote. They also abolished the Black Codes.

One purpose of the Fourteenth Amendment, meanwhile, had been to ensure that freedmen could vote in the former slave states by guaranteeing them citizenship. But, ironically, the Amendment did not explicitly give African Americans the right to vote in those nonslave states in the North that banned it. The Fifteenth Amendment was seen as a remedy for that problem, and such a measure was strongly supported by President Ulysses S. Grant, the former Union general elected in 1869. The Fifteenth Amendment was proposed in Congress in February 1869 and shortly thereafter sent to the states for ratification. By February 1870, enough states had ratified the Fifteenth Amendment that it could be added to the Constitution. Now, no citizen of the United States could be denied the right to vote on the basis of his or her racial or ethnic background, and for the next ten years or so, African Americans took full advantage of their rights. In many localities blacks were elected to serve in many state and local governments. They did so in the face of sometimes violent threats from those who opposed the black vote, most notably the members of the Ku Klux Klan, a white organization that emerged in many states after the Civil War and was often ready to take matters into its own hands with demonstrations, beatings, lynchings, and intimidation at polling places.

By the 1890s attempts to limit African American voting had become widespread. Since citizens could no longer be prevented from voting on the basis of skin color, opponents of black suffrage tried to find other ways to curtail voting rights. Among them were literacy tests, which required anyone who wanted to vote to demonstrate a certain level of ability in reading and writing. African Americans, compared with whites, were much more likely to be illiterate in these years, with many of them still living an isolated rural life. Meanwhile, some localities enacted poll taxes requiring potential voters to pay a fee in order to vote. Again, this restriction fell most heavily on African Americans, who tended to be poorer than whites.

The 1890s also saw the beginning of the Jim Crow era, when many states enacted rules that allowed for legal segregation of blacks and whites. The states were able to do so after the Supreme Court reached a decision in 1896 in *Plessy v. Ferguson*, which permitted "separate but equal" institutions and facilities for blacks and whites. A total of sixteen states and the District of Columbia ultimately enacted Jim Crow laws, resulting in such developments as segregated federal offices under President Woodrow Wilson from 1913 to 1921 and a segregated national army in World War II (1941–1945).

The record of legal challenges to the Fifteenth Amendment during the Jim Crow era was mixed, reflecting the segregationist tone of the era. In 1915, the Supreme Court ruled in *Guinn v. United States* that the new state of Oklahoma could not "grandfather" into its state constitution limits on the right to vote by requiring a literacy test to those who had been citizens, or whose ancestors had been citizens, as of 1866. Such grandfathering in of legislation was often added to literacy tests and poll taxes as a way to limit African American voting.

Meanwhile, in 1935's *Grovey v. Townsend,* the Supreme Court determined that Texas's Democratic Party could prevent African Americans from voting in state primary elections. The Court's reasoning was that the Texas Democratic Party was a private, voluntary organization over which the Fifteenth Amendment held no sway. This decision was overturned, not without reluctance, in 1944's *Smith v. Allwright.*

The Jim Crow era ended in 1954 when the Supreme Court decided in *Brown v. Board of Education* that the principle of "separate but equal" was unconstitutional. The subsequent national civil rights movement helped to produce a wide-ranging Voting Rights Act in 1965. This act is commonly considered to have finally fulfilled the promise of the Fifteenth Amendment by banning literacy tests, poll taxes, and other limits to voting rights. It also gave the federal government oversight authority over jurisdictions that had records of trying to limit African American voting. This challenge to states' rights has been repeatedly upheld, for instance in 1966's *South Carolina v. Katzenbach.* The Voting Rights Act was renewed or amended several times, most recently in 2006, and it will be up for renewal again in 2031.

The Fifteenth Amendment's guarantee of a right to vote faces new challenges in the twenty-first century. In recent elections voters' rights groups have argued that certain procedures are used to discourage African Americans from voting, including the requirement that voters present photo identification and the practice of so-called voter caging.

The right of the state of Indiana to require photo IDs for voters was upheld by the Supreme Court in 2008, and numerous other states have similar requirements. Supporters of the requirement claim that it helps to prevent voter fraud. Opponents claim that it has the effect of limiting the votes of African Americans, who remain, on the whole, poorer than white Americans, as well as of other groups who may not possess photo IDs or even know of the requirement. Some opponents claim that the requirement even amounts to a new poll tax, since state-issued IDs like passports or driver's licenses require that fees be paid.

Voter caging generally consists of ways to challenge voter registrations, the preliminary step in actually voting in elections. One way to do that is to use direct mail lists to target those groups that users might want to prevent from voting. Those groups are sent registered mail, which is automatically returned if the address is not accurate. This then allows for those voters to be directly challenged when the voters reach the polls on the grounds that their registration is invalid. Since fixing such registration problems can be complex and time consuming, especially on election day, caging techniques have the effect of discouraging people from voting. They have been recently used to target African American populations as a way, 138 years after the ratification of the Fifteenth Amendment, to limit their right to vote.

Chronology

1775–1783

The American Revolution, when thirteen British colonies strung along the Atlantic Coast of North America successfully break away from Britain to form the United States of America.

1787

A constitutional convention meets in Philadelphia to begin drafting a Constitution by which the United States of America will be governed. The draft is finished by the end of the year.

1788

The Constitution is ratified by the required nine of the original thirteen states. The tenth state to ratify the Constitution is Virginia, which proposes to add to it a Bill of Rights.

1790

South Carolina limits the vote to white citizens. Most of the rest of the states follow South Carolina's lead over the next years, even new states as they are added to the union.

1791

Congress adds the first ten amendments to the Constitution as the Bill of Rights.

1857

The Supreme Court makes its decision in *Scott v. Sandford*, better known as the Dred Scott case. The Court determines that people of African origin, whether slave or free, cannot be citizens of the United States.

1861–1865

The American Civil War, fought between a "Confederacy" of eleven breakaway Southern states who see their states' rights as being trampled upon by the federal government and a "Union" of mostly Northern and Western states who claim that the Confederacy is unconstitutional. More than six hundred thousand soldiers die in the conflict.

1863

President Abraham Lincoln issues his Emancipation Proclamation, freeing all slaves.

West Virginia becomes the final state to limit the vote to white citizens before the Reconstruction era.

1865

The Civil War ends when Confederate general Robert E. Lee surrenders to his Union counterpart, General Ulysses S. Grant, at the Appomattox, Virginia, courthouse on April 9.

President Abraham Lincoln is assassinated on April 15. He is succeeded by his vice president, Andrew Johnson.

In December, following its ratification by the twenty-seventh of the then thirty-six states, the Thirteenth Amendment is added to the U.S. Constitution. It bans all slavery.

1865–1877

The Reconstruction era, when the United States tries to heal the wounds of the Civil War. Major issues include the reintegration of the Confederate states into the union, the status of former slaves, and the relationship between the federal government and the governments of the states

1866

Congress passes an important Civil Rights Act over President Johnson's veto. Targeting African Americans, it gives U.S. citizenship to "all persons born in the United States not subject to any foreign power, excluding Indians not taxed."

On June 13, the Fourteenth Amendment is proposed to the U.S. Congress.

1868

The Fourteenth Amendment is added to the Constitution on July 28.

Former Union general Ulysses S. Grant is elected president. He hopes to use such measures as a proposed Fifteenth Amendment to finish the process of reconstruction.

1869

In February, the Fifteenth Amendment is proposed and approved by the U.S. Congress, which then sends it on to the states for ratification.

1870

After Georgia, Iowa, Nebraska, and Texas ratify the Fifteenth Amendment in February, it reaches the required three-quarters of the states. Secretary of State Hamilton Fish officially adds it to the Constitution on March 30.

1896

The Supreme Court reaches its decision in *Plessy v. Ferguson*. It uses the principle of "separate but equal" to allow the states to create laws that segregate whites and blacks.

1915

In *Guinn v. United States*, the Supreme Court prevents the new state of Oklahoma from "grandfathering" in voting restrictions that would have had the effect of limiting African Americans' voting privileges.

1935

In *Grovey v. Townsend*, the Supreme Court holds that Texas's Democratic Party can prevent African Americans from voting in its primaries.

1944

In *Smith v. Allwright*, the Supreme Court overturns the *Grovey v. Townsend* decision on the grounds that it violates the Fifteenth Amendment.

1954

In *Brown v. Board of Education*, the Supreme Court overturns *Plessy v. Ferguson*, ending the ability of states to legally segregate schools and other institutions.

1965

The U.S. government enacts a broad Voting Rights Act. It is intended, in part, to prevent states from continuing to use such means as literacy tests to limit the right to vote. The act is amended or renewed in 1970, 1975, 1982, and 2006.

1966

In *South Carolina v. Katzenbach*, the Supreme Court upholds the right of the federal government to review changes in voting procedures in localities where minorities have faced restrictions.

1993

The U.S. government approves the National Voter Registration Act, also known as the Motor Voter law because it allows voters to register at motor vehicle offices.

2000

Republican George W. Bush defeats Democrat Al Gore in a close, controversial presidential election. Among the controversies, centered in Florida, were allegedly inaccurate or inconsistent voting methods in predominantly Democratic areas.

2002

The U.S. government enacts the Help America Vote Act. It is designed to assist localities in modernizing and streamlining voting and registration procedures.

2008

In April, the Supreme Court upholds the right of the state of Indiana to require voters to present photo identification. Opponents fear that such measures will have the effect of disenfranchising poor or minority voters, who are less likely to possess photo identification.

Historical Background on the Fifteenth Amendment

The Fifteenth Amendment Was Part of a "Second Constitution" for the United States

George P. Fletcher

The Fifteenth Amendment was the third of three Reconstruction-era amendments enacted after the United States had been ravaged by the Civil War of 1861–1865. These amendments were largely the work of the most vocal and active political group of the immediate postwar period: the so-called Radical Republicans. But they were also inspired by the wartime president, Abraham Lincoln, who had been assassinated just as the war drew to a close in April 1865. In the following selection, legal scholar George P. Fletcher examines how the three Reconstruction-era amendments amounted to a reordering of America's constitutional structure. Among the most important changes, he notes, was the greater power of the federal government relative to that of the individual states. Another was what was emphasized in the Fifteenth Amendment: the right of all Americans to vote regardless of their ethnic background.

George P. Fletcher is the Cardozo Professor of Jurisprudence at Columbia University.

One year into the [Civil War], after a string of Union defeats, [President Abraham] Lincoln learned that the old Union could not possibly survive. "A new one had to be embraced." And the new Union would have to be based on a new constitutional order. A nation of free Americans, including emancipated slaves, would bear responsibility for rebuilding the United States on the basis of a constitution acceptable to all. Formally speaking, the original charter of 1787 would re-

George P. Fletcher, *Our Secret Constitution: How Lincoln Redefined American Democracy*. Oxford: Oxford University Press, 2001. Copyright © 2001 by George P. Fletcher. Reproduced by permission of Oxford University Press.

main in place, but it would be so radically transformed that it would stand to the *ancien* [old] United States as the *Code civil* [the body of law put in place by the French Revolution (1789–99)] related to the French feudal order [referred to as the *ancien régime*] or as any redeemed legal culture compares to the brutality and chaos that precedes it.

The American hope for a new beginning lay in the Reconstruction Amendments—the Thirteenth, Fourteenth, and Fifteenth—all enacted in quest of a new definition of freedom and equality under the law. The first clause of the Fourteenth Amendment specified who would be a member of the new polity: "All persons born or naturalized in the United States, and subject to the jurisdiction thereof, are citizens of the United States. . . ." With a single stroke the new constitution erased the effects of one of the worst blemishes on American constitutional history—the *Dred Scott* decision of 1857, which held that persons of African descent could never become citizens of the United States. In the new United States, there would be no discrimination based on blood. The only question that mattered was whether you were born within the polity and whether you were therefore likely to come to maturity with the language and consciousness of American culture.

With just boundaries of the new nation-state properly defined, the highest order of business was to define the basic rights of its citizens. The structure of these rights follows the pattern established in the Declaration of Independence: life, liberty, and the pursuit of happiness. Yet, there was a new recognition that the inalienable rights of all Americans were now to be realized not in the state of nature but under the rule of law. The naturalistic "pursuit of happiness," celebrated in the Declaration, gives way to the quintessential creature of the law's definition—property. Yet, the basic rights of life, liberty, and property are inalienable without being absolute. The ideal must be adapted to the practical demands of competing claims. The legal system would have to decide when individu-

The Fifteenth Amendment to the Constitution. It guarantees the right to vote regardless of race. ©Bettmann/Corbis.

als could fairly be deprived of liberty or property or even of life; thus, the coining of the famous and influential clause of the American Constitution, namely that no "State [shall] deprive any person of life, liberty, or Property, without due Process of law." The law would define the content and the limits of the inalienable rights celebrated in the Declaration of Independence.

Duties Incumbent on the States

Also, for the first time, the law would define duties incumbent on the states. The individual state governments must not only guarantee due process for all persons within their jurisdiction, they must also secure "the equal protection of the laws" for all to whom their power extends. True, the original Constitution places some limits on the legislative competence of the states. They must defer to the supremacy of federal law and recognize the privileges and immunities of the citizens of all other states. And there were specific restrictions: They could not enact bills of attainder [declarations of guilt for crimes], ex-post facto laws, or any "law impairing the obligation of contracts." In the postbellum [after the Civil War] constitutional order, however, the states acquired a pervasive duty to treat their residents—those subject to their jurisdiction—decently.

This was a revolutionary change. The states were no longer the autonomous sovereigns that they thought they were when they claimed the right of secession. They were now, in fact, servants of their people. Governments existed to guarantee due process and equal justice for all. The local law was no longer simply a creature of the states. The states themselves were enmeshed in the law and subordinate to it.

In addition to embedding the states in the rule of law, the new constitutional order embarked on an affirmative program to ensure equality among those citizens subject to the jurisdiction of the United States. The heart of the new consensus is that the federal government, victorious in warfare, must continue its aggressive intervention in the lives of its citizens. It must protect the weak against the risk that they would slip into states of subordination resembling the past from which they sought to escape. According to the Thirteenth Amendment, there could never again be relationships of slavery or involuntary servitude in the United States. The federal government would have to be ever watchful to ensure that this kind of slippage would never occur in the private relationships among citizens. Furthermore, under the "equal protection clause," the states must recognize and promote the equality of those subject to their jurisdiction. To round out the commitment to equality, according to the Fifteenth Amendment ratified in 1870, the states could no longer deny voting rights to citizens on the grounds of their race, color, or previous condition of servitude.

New Powers for Congress

These objectives and guarantees are insufficient in themselves to create a constitution, a framework of government. One needs, in addition, a definition of legislative empowerment that would enable the federal government to realize its commitments. This definition is laid down in all three of the postbellum amendments. All three grant the power to Congress to enforce the basic framework "with appropriate legislation." True, the new Congress takes as a given many of the provisions of the original Constitution. The new order inherits an operating Congress, Executive, and Judiciary. They would be recast in new functions, but the forms remained the same.

The argument, then, is that the three Reconstruction Amendments enacted a second American constitution. The terms of this constitution, as culled from the amendments— with some rearrangement and leaving out historically specific clauses—can be stated in a few words:

§1. All persons born or naturalized in the United States, and subject to the jurisdiction thereof, are citizens of the United States and of the State wherein they reside.

§2. No State shall make or enforce any law which shall abridge the privileges or immunities of citizens of the United States.

§3. No State shall deprive any person of life, liberty, or property, without due process of law.

§4. No State shall deny to any person within its jurisdiction the equal protection of the laws.

§5. Neither slavery nor involuntary servitude, except as a punishment for crime whereof the party shall have been duly convicted, shall exist within the United States.

§6. The right of citizens of the United States to vote shall not be denied or abridged by the United States or by any State on account of race, color, or previous condition of servitude.

§7. The Congress shall have power to enforce the foregoing provisions by appropriate legislation.

These seven propositions summarize the enduring content of the Reconstruction Amendments. The key provisions of these amendments define political membership, articulate basic rights, and provide an ambit of legislative competence. So reformed, the American system of government would be able to protect individual rights as well as promote the equality of all persons who survived the war.

The Ratification of the Fifteenth Amendment Helped Former Rebel States Rejoin the Union

Brooks D. Simpson

In the following selection, historian Brooks D. Simpson explores the political context behind the ratification of the Fifteenth Amendment. The amendment was a product of the Reconstruction era (1865–1878), when leaders tried to rebuild the American Union in the aftermath of the Civil War. One cause of that war was the rights of individual states in relation to the federal government, and that issue remained close to the top of politicians' lists of concerns during Reconstruction.

Simpson's main focus in this excerpt is on the full return to the Union of a number of Southern states during the first years of the presidency of former Union general Ulysses S. Grant, who was in office from 1869 to 1877. Several of those states, indeed, remained under military occupation in 1869. Grant was very concerned with reconciling the interests of the so-called Radical Republicans in his party with those of more conservative Republicans, a number of whom emerged from the South. One tactic that he used in a careful juggling act was to require any state desiring full representation at the national level to ratify the Fifteenth Amendment.

Brooks D. Simpson is professor of history and humanities at Arizona State University.

In his inaugural address, [President Ulysses S.] Grant called upon Americans to approach reconstruction "calmly, without prejudice, hate, or sectional pride, remembering that the greatest good to the greatest number is the object to be attained." That statement reassured those southern whites who welcomed his rise to power. [Senator] Augustus Garland of Arkansas believed that Grant could "rescue us from destruction, and lay broad, deep, and permanent, the foundation for our own future well being." Possibly the new president "might surround himself with decent, moderate and able men of the republican party" whose moderate principles would guide policy. Grant, after all, had never been identified with the Radical wing of the Republican party, and many Radicals had grudgingly accepted his nomination. "It is our true policy, it seems to me, to extend to Gen'l Grant a 'generous confidence' as the best mode of winning his favor," conservative Herschel V. Johnson told [former Confederate vice president and now Georgia representative] Alexander H. Stephens. If Grant was "just and generous, . . . the great Southern heart, warm, magnanimous and brave, will leap for joy and throb with gratitude," he declared. Others agreed. Virginians, reported one resident of the Old Dominion, "are favorably disposed toward Genl. Grant," believing that the incoming president "is free from rancorous feelings toward the South." Grant's "independent course is calculated to inspire the South with hope and confidences" one Texan remarked. There was political wisdom in winning white support, for, as the editor of the Springfield (Mass.) *Republican*, Samuel Bowles, observed, "The Republican party cannot long maintain its supremacy in the South by negro votes alone."

At the same time, Grant advocated the "security of person, property, and free religious and political opinion in every part of our common country, without regard to local prejudice." Behind such platitudes he pledged to press for black rights. North Carolina governor William Holden told blacks that Grant's election "has given you practical assurance of your freedom." White terrorists no longer posed a threat. Grant's victory grounded the nation "so securely on the principles of Freedom and Justice that hereafter we may fear nothing."

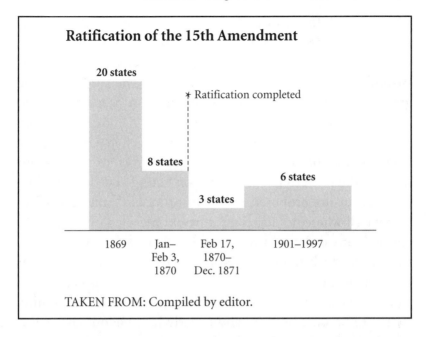

Ratification of the 15th Amendment

TAKEN FROM: Compiled by editor.

Once again the fundamental ambiguity present in "Let us have peace" appeared—although Grant did not see it. Others might portray him as either a supporter of conciliation with whites or as a supporter of black rights. Grant thought he could be both. His initial cabinet veered toward moderate assumptions about reconstruction, even after he had to name early replacements for the State and Treasury Departments. Hamilton Fish (secretary of state) was a conservative Republican, while George Boutwell (treasury secretary) had long been identified with the Radicals; if Interior Secretary Jacob D. Cox and Attorney General Ebenezer R. Hoar were not deeply committed to reconstruction, Maryland's John Creswell (postmaster general) was. "The Southern Radicals are delighted with Creswell's nomination," enthused the abolitionist New York *Independent*. "He was their choice, and is to the last drop of blood in his veins a through Radical Republican."

Ending Military Rule in Three States

Grant first moved to the center when he addressed the status of the three states still under military supervision: Mississippi,

Virginia, and Texas. In each state, Republicans worked to bar former Confederates from participation in the new regimes, but a majority of voters proved unwilling to support that position. If Grant placated centrist whites, he might lay the groundwork for broadening the Republican base of support. The first concrete move toward realignment took place when a delegation of white Virginians approached Grant. They would accept black suffrage and equality before the law but rejected the proscriptive measures on voting and officeholding included in the proposed state constitution. Grant acceded to a proposal whereby such clauses would be voted on separately, and forwarded the idea to Congress. "It is desirable to restore the States which were engaged in the rebellion to their proper relations to the Government and the country at as early a period as the people of those States should be found willing [both] to become peaceful and orderly [and] adopt and maintain such constitutions and laws as will effectually secure the civil and political rights of all persons within their borders," he argued. . . . He urged that Mississippians be allowed the same option in a second ratification vote. Three days later Congress complied, adding Texas to the list of states where Grant could call for the separate submission of these proscriptive clauses. However, it added one new requirement: each state would have to ratify the Fifteenth Amendment before its representatives would be seated.

Virginians would vote first under the terms of Grant's proposal. State Republicans were divided over whether to push for the proscriptive clauses, exposing a division in that party's ranks that would reappear elsewhere in the years to come. Radical Republicans held firm to the idea of exclusion; moderates and conservatives, looking to attract native white voters, opposed it. Grant favored the moderate position, having been reassured by no less an authority than [former Confederate general] Robert E. Lee that white Virginians would accept black suffrage and the results of the war. In July, the Radicals suffered defeat. The proscriptive clauses were voted down; Gilbert C. Walker, a native Virginian who stood as the Conservative Republican candidate, won over his Radical opponent; Conservative Republicans and Democrats secured a majority in the state legislature, although 29 of the 183 legislators were black. Some northern Republicans protested the result; others either praised or acquiesced in the result. "We can't back out of the results of a fair submission, under authority of Congress and the Administration, of the constitution of Virginia," observed Cox. Better to secure Virginia's vote for the Fifteenth Amendment, "so that we may take a last affectionate farewell of the Reconstruction."

Grant was not so pleased. In wanting moderate Republicans to win the day, he did not look to hand the state over to the Democrats. And yet he could not protest too much, for the elections had been peaceful and fair. The restoration of civil government did not necessarily mean the continuation of Republican rule. The following month, Grant permitted the state legislature to convene without requiring its members to take the test oath, thus allowing legislators to avoid disqualification. However, in Tennessee, Republican chances to retain power crumbled because of party factionalism. Conservative Republican DeWitt Senter, who had assumed the governorship when incumbent William G. Brownlow won election to the U.S. Senate at the beginning of the year, sought to retain the office; state Radicals supported the candidacy of William B. Stokes. Senter bolstered his majorities by helping ex-Confederates dodge disfranchisement, most notably by appointing new registrars who chose not to ask too many questions. Democrats supported Senter and concentrated their efforts on securing control of the legislature. In August they claimed victory and prepared to undo the policies of their predecessors.

Careful Politics

What happened in Tennessee illustrated for Republicans the risks of wooing conservative support. A similar result in Mississippi and Texas would damage the Republican party in both the South and the nation. Grant publicly shifted his support to regular Republicans when he spurned the efforts of a Mississippi fusion movement to secure his support by nominating as their gubernatorial candidate Lewis Dent, the president's brother-in-law. Mississippi Republicans triumphed in the fall elections, although the proscriptive clauses fell, and moderates controlled the party. Texas proved more challenging. Although proscription was not an issue, Republican factionalism was especially intense. Grant relied on an old West Point classmate, district commander Joseph J. Reynolds, to advise him on what to do; Reynolds eventually sided with the Radicals. For several months the president wavered between Radicals and moderates, hoping that the two factions would work out their differences. When Democrats decided to support the moderates in an effort to repeat what had happened in Virginia, Grant threw the administration whole-heartedly behind the candidacy of Radical Edmund J. Davis, who won in a close contest.

These attempts to define a vital center in southern politics conducive to Republicanism had produced mixed results. Conciliation in Virginia had delivered the Old Dominion to a coalition of conservative Republicans and Democrats; in Texas, the failure of party factions to find common ground had led to a Radical triumph. Only in Mississippi had Grant seen both moderation and Republicanism triumph. Different circumstances in each state suggested that it would be difficult for the president to take a uniform approach. However, if he tailored policy to fit individual circumstances, the result would contain contradictions and tensions, leading unwary observers to conclude that he had no policy at all.

When Congress convened in December 1869, Grant urged it to recognize the new state governments of Virginia, Texas, and Mississippi "and thus close the work of reconstruction." But Republicans in Congress divided over whether they could or should impose requirements on Virginia before readmitting the state, with Radicals pushing for the taking of the test oath of the Fourteenth Amendment by Virginia officeholders and a promise not to alter the state constitution in ways adverse to black suffrage, civil rights, and education. Perhaps some Radicals wanted to block Virginia's readmission by raising the reservations; the Virginians shrewdly gave way, confident that once the state was readmitted, Congress would be unable to check subsequent developments. The readmission of Mississippi and Texas proved less troublesome because Republicans were unquestionably in power.

Elsewhere Grant demonstrated his concern with the fate of black Americans, having assured a delegation of black Tennesseans that he "would do all in his power to protect them." First was the problem of political violence in Georgia. Republicans there had started off well—so well, in fact, that Georgia's Democrats decided to put a stop to it after the Republicans secured victory in the April 1868 state contests. Democrats had successfully purged the state legislature of black representatives; Republican factionalism further damaged the party's fortunes. That fall, Democratic-supported political terrorism targeted Republican voters, black and white. . . .

Grant remained silent about Georgia throughout the first several months of his administration because it served his interests in encouraging moderate approaches in Virginia, Texas, and Mississippi. In December, he called upon Congress to enable Georgia's governor, Rufus Bullock, to convene the original legislature and disqualify those members who were not eligible to hold office under the terms of the Fourteenth Amendment. Congress agreed, mandating ratification of the Fifteenth Amendment as a prerequisite to readmission. Grant went further and remanded the state to military supervision, arguing that congressional action revived the supervisory structure outlined in the Reconstruction Acts. However, he became restive when Bullock sought to use the opportunity of reorganizing the state government to push forward several initiatives. If Republicanism was to survive in Georgia, it would have to demonstrate that it could do so without the protection of federal bayonets. Radicals lost their bid to postpone elections for the state legislature from 1870 to 1872, which would have given Bullock and his followers increased leverage. Grant himself urged Congress to reach some accord on Georgia, for, as one newspaper noted, he was "very solicitous that the whole reconstruction business shall be ended immediately." Vice President [Schuyler] Colfax revealed the administration's increasing skepticism about Georgia, wishing a delegation of black Georgians good luck in their struggle to maintain Republican rule even as he openly wondered whether the legislature could sustain itself.

Pushing the Fifteenth Amendment

To enable blacks to shape their own future at the ballot box, Grant pushed for the ratification of the Fifteenth Amendment. Immediately after the war he questioned whether it was time to enfranchise blacks until the persistence of white southern recalcitrance convinced him that blacks had to be given the means to defend themselves at the polls. Unhappy with the hypocrisy inherent in Republican efforts to mandate black suffrage in the South while leaving it up to each northern state to accept it, Grant saw in the Fifteenth Amendment a way to erase the color line at the ballot box. Its adoption would secure black voting rights in the South and end the mostly futile process attending efforts to bring about the enfranchisement of blacks in the North. It was not clear whether the amendment would increase narrow Republican majorities in several key states, since white backlash might more than nullify the augmentation of Republican strength. Grant believed that with the passage of the amendment debate over southern policy would fade into the background, and before long parties and voters would turn to new issues. With that in mind, he urged ratification in his inaugural [address].

Grant closely followed the course of the ratification struggle. He urged Nebraska's governor to call a special session to secure ratification there, "in order that it may no longer remain an open issue, and a subject of agitation before the people"; he twisted arms to gain Nevada's assent. He even contemplated rushing through the readmission of Georgia and Texas, complete with their ratification of the amendment, in time to enfranchise blacks for spring elections in Connecticut. In March he took the unusual step of commemorating the amendment's ratification by issuing a proclamation that characterized it as a complete repudiation of the Dred Scott decision [of 1857] that blacks had no rights that whites were bound to respect. The amendment was "a measure of grander importance than any other one act of the kind from the foundation of our free government to the present day." He reminded blacks of "the importance of their striving in every honorable manner to make themselves worthy of their new privilege" while advising whites, "the race more favored heretofore by our laws," to "withhold no privilege of advancement to the new citizen." The president called upon Congress to assist the emancipated in their quest for advancement through support for public education. Failing to act on this suggestion, Congress even considered terminating the Bureau of Education but backed down when Grant pointed out, "With millions of ex-slaves to be educated, now is not the time to suppress an office for facilitating education."

Completing Reconstruction

"The issues of the rebellion and the war pass away," proclaimed the Washington (D.C.) *National Republican* on the eve of ratification. The past five years had witnessed a veritable revolution in the republic's constitutional framework. It was time to rest and take stock. "The present generation must rest content with knowing that so far as legal principles are involved, the process of reconstruction has reached its limits in the legislation of 1869," that political pundit of distinguished pedigree, Henry Adams, remarked. Republicans far more committed to social justice than Adams agreed. "It is not the theory of [our] government that any able-bodied citizen shall be carried, but that none shall be impeded in the fair and equal race of life," declared Congressman James A. Garfield. To the Ohio Republican, the Fifteenth Amendment "confers upon the African Race the care of its own destiny. It places their fortunes in their own hands." This achievement, he thought, was enough. "The South ought now to be dropped by Congress," declared the *Nation*, a journal with Radical roots that was having second thoughts. "All that paper and words can do for it have been done." Others echoed that sentiment. "It is the general feeling that we have done enough, gone far enough in governmental reconstruction, and that it is best for all that the southern communities should be left to manage themselves," concluded one Ohioan. The *New York Times* asserted that "now that reconstruction is at the very point of completion, there ought to be no need of additional laws." It warned that "the utmost caution should be observed in the exercise of the Executive prerogative," for any mis-step would provide Grant's opponents with "ground for cavil and complaint."

Grant initially believed that the ratification of the Fifteenth Amendment went a long way to completing reconstruction. He had even considered issuing a general amnesty in his proclamation celebrating ratification but continuing antiblack violence caused him to withhold it. There were other things he could do to enhance black opportunity. One was to protect blacks from violence, so that bullets could not stifle ballots. Another was to arm black Americans with yet another tool, economic clout.

The Fifteenth Amendment Is Simply Justice

Benjamin F. Whittemore

Congressional approval of the Fifteenth Amendment was helped along by a number of Southern members of the Republican Party who were ready to work with their Northern counterparts to complete the work of reconstruction. One such congressman was Benjamin F. Whittemore, whose speech of January 28, 1869, in the House of Representatives makes up the following selection. In his speech, Whittemore asserts that the Fifteenth Amendment is fully justified given America's history of favoring equality. He notes that many African Americans served, and some died, in Civil War armies and that by ensuring that African Americans have the right to vote, the government can help to heal the wounds of the war.

Benjamin F. Whittemore served South Carolina in the House of Representatives from 1868 to 1870.

Mr. Speaker, the work is before us; the past instructs us; the present admonishes, and the future awaits the result of our action—the performance of duty; to know whether we have learned wisdom by experience, and can deal justly; whether we have determined "to treat our neighbors as ourselves;" to acknowledge certain great truths self-evident, and give to others the immunities we claim—franchise and protection. The war abolished slavery with its sum of villainies; let Congress abolish political heresies and piratical invasions upon human rights; then will equal justice be established, and a peace that can alone be prosperous and permanent throughout the Republic; then will security be guarantied the humblest citizen, and a unity of States that can never be severed by

Benjamin F. Whittemore, "Speech Before the House of Representatives," *The Congressional Globe*, January 28, 1869. The Library of Congress.

CELEBRATION AT BALTIMORE ON MAY 19ᵗʰ 1870.

THE FIFTEENTH AMENDMENT AND ITS RESULTS.

Respectfully dedicated to the colored Citizens of the U.S. of America. A.D. 1870. by Schneider & Fuchs 184 N. Eutaw St. Baltimore M?

A lithograph depicting the foreseeable results of the passage of the Fifteenth Amendment, which established the principles that a state cannot "deprive any person of life, liberty, or property, without due process of law." Standard RM/© Corbis.

dissensions from within or invasions from without. Centuries are to look at our work effectually done or shamefully neglected. Let us be found equal to our task, prompt in our action, united in the cause of universal emancipation from wrong, and the acceptation of the right. The nation must award equal political privileges to all men everywhere, all over the wide extent of our common country.

A Speedy Settlement

Such a course will, as the honorable gentleman from Massachusetts [Mr. Boutwell] so truly declared, become the means of a speedy settlement of all the vexatious questions that have divided us in the past. Whatever may be said in opposition to the measure now before us, or its unconstitutionality; however much lawyers may differ in their interpretation of statutory provisions, though we may exhaust research, compile the assertions of men that agree or disagree on the rights of a citizen or what constitutes a citizen, enter into the most elaborate analysis of the law and strive to create a holy reverence for ourselves and a grave indifference for others; though we may quote Patrick Henry, [Thomas] Jefferson, [James] Madison, Chief Justice [John] Marshall . . . the oldest or the youngest of the learned in the jurisprudence of our country to prop up the old systems and errors which have created greater regard for the State than for the nation, still we are forced by the circumstances around us to acknowledge that the bone of contention will never be removed while we prate [discuss excessively] the law and withhold justice.

Do you wish to end the controversy—settle the difficulty in the minds of those who have steadily opposed congressional reconstruction in the South? Do you propose to encourage and protect loyalty there? Then, as this bill provides, give the benefits of the franchise to every citizen in every State, without regard to race, color, or previous condition. Such a course will close the mouths of the sternest opponents of "the forced franchise," where the largest number of the colored men in our country are found. You cannot blame men of the South when they come with their accusations of inconsistency, laying them at your doors, if you still adhere to partial legislation and do not accept for yourselves what you have imposed upon them.

Shall a new sectional difficulty be created now that we have been delivered from one great curse which so nearly ruined our national existence; while the North by its prowess and championship for the right in one great issue dared to do or die that the wrong should be overcome, slavery abolished, the Union saved? Shall it falter in its action now? Shall we fail to recognize our duty to those who rallied to our standards that they might prove by their valor, devotion, suffering, death, their right to all the immunities of an American citizen? Shall we trust the pardoned rebel and not the patriot black man, whose severed limb lies moldering at [Civil War battle sites] Fort Pillow, Port Hudson, Olustee, Battery Wagner, or Petersburg mine? Shall we refuse, because the remnants of degenerate philosophies or theories hang upon the verge of our Government, to declare the infamous codes of the past, false to the grand and glorious enunciations of universal justice, or to act the part of statesmen worthy of the hour—the nation's glorious opportunity?

True Equality

Give to the colored man his vote. He has a national equality with you; he is an American citizen, a veteran of the field on which through bloody contests triumph alone has come, that enables us this day to legislate for an undivided country. On staff and crutch he stands demanding his rights; with scars and empty sleeves he pleads an equal franchise; with uplifted hands, which have borne the musket in the defense of your altars and your homes, of that flag, emblem of freedom, of the future greatness of our Republic, he asks, not social, but political equality. Give the colored man his vote; then and not till then will disloyalty be crushed; then and not till then will tranquility become the boon of our people; then and not till then will the material which feeds the flame of partisan and sectional strife be removed forever. This is no longer a white man's Government; it is a government for all the people; black men have rights that white men are now enjoined to respect. They have the largest number of them given their ballots in the last election for the hero and chieftain, General Grant. With true loyalty in their hearts and Grant ballots in their hands they have exercised a freeman's will and united with yourselves in securing the era of peace.

It is said there are only one hundred and sixty thousand colored men yet to be enfranchised; about the number that were enrolled of their race in the Union armies. Surely if we could intrust them with the bullet why should we longer withhold from them the ballot? Why need we falter? Is there not in the constitution of our nature something that speaks louder and more earnest than the voice of prejudice or caste or false legislation, which tells us that now is the most favorable time for the settlement of a question so momentous?

"Then let us act wisely, we've nothing to fear,

The voice of the people is heard far and near

That manhood, not color, must be the sole test

Of a right to the franchise, North, South, East, and West."

I concur in all that my learned and honored friend from Massachusetts has said. I believe, with him, we cannot afford to do wrong. The Constitution, which we regard as the fundamental basis of national law and equity, makes it our imperative duty to guaranty to every man who claims himself an American citizen the benefits of a republican form of government. Is that Government republican which creates and maintains distinctions in franchise; that gives the vote to one and withholds it from another? The Government was founded on the principle that man was endowed by his Creator with certain inalienable rights; that all men were created equal; not a portion to rule by a divine right and others to be ruled by the usurpations of might *nolens volens* [whether unwillingly or willingly] that the Government derived its just powers from the consent of the governed. Our fathers, out of their own experience in framing the Magna Charta, intended to denounce the dogmas of kings and tyrants and to establish as the cardinal, central idea of their declarations that the people were the sovereigns, deriving from God himself the right to say who should rule over them and what form of government they would have. They start out with the bold language, "We, the people"—not the white nor the black—"do ordain and establish this Constitution for the United States of America"—not for Massachusetts, not for Pennsylvania, not for Maryland or Virginia, but "for the United States;" and among the reasons given why they have thus ordained are these: "to form a more perfect union, establish justice, promote the general welfare, and secure the blessings of liberty to ourselves and posterity."

Now, then, can our liberty be secure in the hands of those who question our rights? Who is secure in his freedom when debarred from saying what kind of men shall represent him? Can we believe that the one hundred and sixty thousand colored men would give, if they are invested with the franchise, their ballots for those who cast their voice, influence, argument, and vote against this measure? They are, whether acknowledged or not, the constituencies of such as will seal their destinies by their action on the grand proposition before us. As for myself, I am ready to make our fathers' words no empty boast. By all that is just, by the remembrance of past antagonisms, by the rights we enjoy, hold sacred and inviolate; by the measurements of a golden rule, that principle which should govern us in our actions and control us in our legislation, having found that there is that in our statutes destructive of the essential features of a republican form of government, let us accept "the right to alter or to abolish" all unrepublican features of such statutes and adhere to such principles as shall seem most likely to effect the safety and happiness of all the people.

Voting Rights Should Be Preserved for White Men of European Background

James R. Doolittle

In the following selection, Republican senator from Wisconsin James R. Doolittle states his reasons for opposing the Fifteenth Amendment during congressional debates on the subject. At the heart of Doolittle's thinking was his belief that African Americans were truly a different people than white Americans and, echoing the racial philosophies then growing widespread in his day, his belief that the two races should not mix. He claims that African Americans, for the most part, are not "competent" to vote and that they may be more suited to the climates of the West Indies than those of the United States. He also expresses concern that the proposed amendment might be unfair to the Southern states since more of their total population is African American as compared with the states of the North.

James R. Doolittle served as a U.S. senator from 1857 to 1869.

Mr. President, the amendment as proposed by the committee had something like generality, and in the discussion of the question we had to discuss it upon general principles without reference to any particular race or nationality. But this proposition brings it directly to the point, so far as the African is concerned in the United States; and that, as a matter of course, raises the question at once as to the propriety and justice of this Government forcing upon the States by a constitutional amendment the African vote.

I believe all observing men agree, not only outside of the Senate, but Senators will agree in private conversation, I have

James R. Doolittle, "Speech Before Congress," *The Congressional Globe*, February 8, 1869. The Library of Congress.

no doubt, if you sit down with them and talk it over, that while as a general rule white men are competent to vote, yet, as a general rule with some exceptions, the Africans are incompetent to vote. Some of our friends from the lately reconstructed States may perhaps demur a little to this general declaration. . . .

But take the gentlemen from any of those States where they have practical knowledge of the African race as it is, and among the white men of sense in this country there is not one in ten who, if you will, sit down by his side and get into his interior thoughts and conversation, will not tell you that, as a general rule, the Africans are incompetent to vote. We know it. Everybody knows it.

What is the occasion of that incompetency? It is not a matter of a day nor a year nor a generation. It is a matter of six thousand years and the whole history of the race. Men speak of the question as a question of skin. I have heard my honorable friend from Massachusetts hour by hour denounce the oligarchy of the skin, as if the skin was not mentioned simply as one of the incidents of the race, to distinguish it from other races; whereas everybody who knows anything on the subject knows, all natural philosophy teaches, all ethnologists, all historians, all men who know by actual experience anything of this race knows that the skin is by no means the greatest distinction between the African and the white man. From the hair on the top of his head to the soles of his feet there is not an organ in his body in which there is not as much distinction between him and the white man as there is in his skin. From the wool which grows upon his head to the soles of his feet, in his interior organs, his kidneys, his stomach, his bones, his body, his interior mental and moral organization, he exhibits throughout just as great distinctions as the skin. The fiat of the Almighty has written it, and the experience of the world proves it. He cannot be amalgamated with the white race and produce a third race or a yellow race.

Amalgamation may go on illicitly; there may be offspring, but the whole history of the medical world shows that this offspring is enfeebled, with neither the power of the white man nor the power of the black man, and that in a short period he ceases to propagate his species. It is the fiat of the Almighty which is stamped upon this very idea of forcing an amalgamation of the races against nature and against the laws of God. Those who attempt to do it are warring against all history and warring against the laws of Him that made history and made the races of men.

Truly Different Races

Why, sir, how does this race appear in the States of the South, and in Africa, too? We often quote here the language of Jefferson declaring for the equality of the rights of men. We all agree to that. But Jefferson also declares, with as much distinctness and with as much force as he declares the natural rights of men, that it is impossible for you to put these two races together and maintain them upon a footing of equality side by side in the same Government. Your experience has demonstrated it. In the States in the South you, sir, (Mr. Welch in the chair,) know, and there is not a man in the Senate who does not know that the irrepressible conflict of race—not a conflict in arms, for the power of the Federal Government prevents that, but a conflict of race, irrepressible, constant, eternal—is going on between the blacks and the whites, as it is going on between the whites and the Indians on the frontier. They may blind their eyes if they please to these facts, but they are as bright as the sunlight everywhere. Just so long as the effort is made to enforce an unnatural equality between the white race and an alien and inferior race, an exotic race which does not belong in the temperate zones of the earth, which has been brought here from the tropics where God planted it and intended it to stay, and from which the cupidity of man has wrenched him from his native position and forced him into this exotic condition in the soil of the United States, so long will this warfare go on, because you are attempting to enforce this unnatural equality upon the States of the South against their will.

Mr. President, in the midst of all this trouble some events are transpiring which may bring a solution to this conflict of race, as I hope it may, without any bloody conflict of arms. Upon our southern border there are tropical climates already inhabited by the colored race and where the colored man is adapted by constitution and nature to live. There are San Domingo and Hayti and Cuba, which will probably soon abolish slavery; and all the islands of the West Indies, which, in the process of time, may come under the jurisdiction of this Government, may be held under its flag, and I hope they will be. Those islands where the white race is doomed because the white race is not adapted to the climate and cannot live there may become, under the providence of God, a home for the Africans in the United States who have the intelligence and the enterprise to migrate to those islands, and there live among their own people by themselves, and thus withdraw from that conflict of race which is constant, irrepressible, eternal, while they undertake to live under the same Government with the white man, side by side, upon a footing of equality.

The West Indies

The newspapers speak, and therefore I am at liberty to refer to it, of a treaty negotiated between this Government and Denmark for the island of St. Thomas. For one, I do not hesitate to avow that I hope, if such a treaty has been negotiated, it will be ratified and confirmed. The island of St. Thomas contains the best harbor almost in the Gulf of Mexico. It is the entrepot [entry] to the West Indies, the outside island and harbor which flanks them all, and its acquisition will secure to us in the end all the islands of the Gulf of Mexico and the West Indies. I say, for one, I hope that such a treaty, if negotiated, will be accepted and confirmed by the Government of the United States; and, further, that the other islands of the Gulf one after another will be acquired by the Government of the United States. . . .

I said the conflict was eternal; I was speaking of course of temporal affairs; eternal on this earth so long as the races are brought in contact with each other.

I was saying, Mr. President, that I hope this Government will acquire these islands in the West Indies, and that they will become the home of the colored men of the United States, who can emigrate to them gradually, not all at once, not all in one year or in ten years, and perhaps never all emigrating to those islands, but where the emigration can begin, transferring our language, our influence, and our colored men to the building up in those islands of American interests, and interests which shall be in harmony with the Republic of the United States; where we can establish territorial governments as we have established a territorial government or given a territory to the Indian tribes under our jurisdiction; where our flag can protect them; where a few of our own troops stationed in fortifications would give steadiness to the territorial governments which these colored men can administer for themselves under our guarantee and our protection; where they will be withdrawn from this conflict with the superior and dominant race, under whose influence, if you press forward the measures which you are presenting now, endeavoring to force them on a footing of equality everywhere with the white man—this weak, this feeble, this inferior, this subject, this dependent race will be trampled in the dust as certain as we see the red man of the forest being trampled under the foot of the Anglo-Saxon.

If we would preserve the colored man from destruction, we must open such an outlet that he may escape from this conflict of race which is bearing him down everywhere. I know gentlemen may say he is not borne down now in the

States of the South. Why? Because the whole power of the Federal Government with its armies is there. You defend him by force of arms. I do not speak of a conflict of arms between the blacks and the whites. I mean that other conflict, that moral conflict, that conflict in the marts of trade, in the marts of business, in the marts of commerce, where side by side with the white man he is not his equal in the competition of life, and where he must and will go down. Give to him a home in the tropical regions of the West Indies; give to him a country where the white man cannot live and labor, and there he will be secure. That, sir, may be the true solution of this difficulty in which we are placed; that may be the solution of this conflict of race between the whites and the blacks. But it is not a solution of that conflict to undertake by force of arms to force him upon a footing of equality with the white men of the South or the white men of any other States in the Union, and at the same time it is breaking down what has been regarded as one of the rights of the States from the beginning, as sacred and secure as any other, to wit: that each State for itself should control this whole question of suffrage.

African Americans and Chinese Migrants

But, sir, there is another objection to this amendment. We know that with the completion of the Pacific railroad our commerce between our western shores and Asia will be doubled, trebled, quadrupled; that with every returning ship hundreds and thousands, it may be hundred of thousands, of laboring men from China, and Japan, and the great fountain of human population in Asia, will be brought to the United States. There are one hundred thousand Chinamen now on our western coast. In ten years there may be a million. In ten years there may be as many Chinamen as there are white men there. Under the principle for which you contend of the equality of the races of men in the administration of the political affairs of this Government, how can you contend in favor of giving this power to the African race if you deny it to the Chinese? You know that the Chinese are far in advance of the African in point of civilization. You know that, in comparison with the Chinaman, the African is inferior. You know that in point of industry the testimony of all men upon the western coast in relation to the Chinaman is that he loves industry; that he loves to labor. He is trained to labor and habits of industry and habits of frugality and economy that are most remarkable.

If we are to carry out the idea for which gentlemen contend of the equality of all races before the law and before the Constitution of the United States in taking part in the Government of the country, if we are to extend these privileges to the African, why should we not extend them to the Chinaman? Give me a reason, if you can. And yet we know that all the Senators from the western coast are unanimously opposed to extending any such rights to the Chinaman. You know that when the treaty with China was confirmed the idea of admitting Chinamen to naturalization, I believe, was unanimously opposed by the majority of the Senate.

How can you stand upon this ground, and yet insist on forcing the African in this country on a footing of equality with the white man? Why not stand upon the principle one way or the other? Either stand, as I stand, maintaining that while slavery should be abolished and every man should be protected in his rights, and we should give to the negro just as much protection as we give to an Englishman or to an Irishman or to a German, when he comes to this country, remaining here an alien and a foreigner, giving him the same protection in property and person that we give to more than a million, probably, of foreigners who are now residing in the United States, half a million residing in New England who have no right to vote at all, and yet they are protected in every right, protected in their families, protected in their property, protected by the laws of the United States and by the laws of the several States. Put the negro upon that ground; make him a freeman; establish his freedom, give him the same protection which other men have under the law, but do not undertake to force the Government of the United States or the government of the States into his hands. Either do that or adopt the principles that are in favor of giving universal equality and political power to all the races in the United States, including the Chinese.

State Differences

Mr. President, there may, in the course of human events, arise some other questions and qualification which it would be very desirable to apply in the States of the Union, and therefore the necessity, in my opinion, of leaving this question of suffrage to be determined by the several States, for the States may differ in their situation. While I am opposed to the principle contained in the constitution of Rhode Island, I admit the right of the State to fix the qualifications of her voters, because I admit that on that subject she has a right under the Constitution to do it. What is the qualification in Rhode Island? No foreign-born citizen is allowed to vote unless he is the owner of real estate. No man born in Europe can vote in Rhode Island until he becomes a freeholder in Rhode Island. That is a restrictive qualification on the part of Rhode Island that I do not justify, while, at the same time, I admit that Rhode Island has the power to impose such a restriction. Massachusetts imposes another, to wit, that no person shall be permitted to vote unless he can read the Constitution of the United States in the English language. That substantially excludes every foreign-born citizen who does not read the English language. It excludes, as a matter of course, every negro who cannot read the English language. If you were to apply the qualification which is required in Massachusetts in South Carolina to-day, under this amendment proposed by the Senator from Michigan, I suppose four fifths, if not nine tenths, of all the negro population in South Carolina would be excluded. The State of New York applies to the colored man a different kind of qualification. If he is possessed and owns in his own right $250 worth of property he is permitted to vote, not because the property has any right to vote, but because a colored man who shows capacity enough to acquire and hold $250 worth of property shows that he is an exception among the colored race, and he being among the exceptions has a right to vote. This is the doctrine of New York. You may take the doctrine of Vermont. There are very few negroes living in Vermont, and it requires so much capacity on the part of a negro to get to Vermont and live there after he does get there [laughter] that the very fact of his living there shows that he is an exception among his race and has some capacity which might entitle him to the privilege of voting. And so it is with all the other extreme northern States.

But, sir, when you come down to the middle States, where the climate is milder, or go into the southern States, where they can live and thrive almost upon productions of the soil without much industry, you will find a very different state of things; and in those States a different qualification may be necessary to be applied. If they were to apply the qualification of Massachusetts perhaps that would be all that would be necessary to exclude from suffrage the great mass of the colored men, and that they can do under the proposition proposed by the Senator from Michigan. I certainly do not oppose his amendment on that ground, because I believe in allowing the States to make those qualifications.

The Fifteenth Amendment Will Help Blacks Fulfill Their Potential as Americans

Frederick Douglass

The following selection is excerpted from a speech given in 1870 by Frederick Douglass (1818–1895), a former slave and one of the era's foremost proponents of rights for freed slaves and African Americans in general. He made the speech after learning of the final ratification of the Fifteenth Amendment guaranteeing African Americans the right to vote.

In this speech, Douglass notes that the Fifteenth Amendment not only guarantees voting rights for African Americans (as well as other nonwhite, non-Christian citizens), it enhances the freedom of all. It does so by ensuring that citizens can take full responsibility for their own opportunities and accomplishments. In a statement foreshadowing one made in a 1965 speech by another African American leader, Dr. Martin Luther King Jr., Douglass claims that "character, not color, is to be the criterion" of one's fortunes.

I have no fixed and formal speech to make to you to-day. The event we celebrate is its own best speech. It exceeds all speech, and language is tame in its presence. It has rolled in upon us a joyous surprise, and seems almost too good to be true.

You did not expect to see it; I did not expect to see it; no man living did expect to live to see this day. In our moments of unusual mental elevation and heart-longings, some of us may have caught glimpses of it afar off; we saw it only by the strong, clear, earnest eye of faith, but none dared even to hope to stand upon the earth at its coming. Yet here it is. Our eyes behold it; our ears hear it, our hearts feel it, and there is no doubt or illusion about it. The black man is free, the black man is a citizen, the black man is enfranchised, and this by the organic law of the land. No more a slave, no more a fugitive slave, no more a despised and hated creature, but a man, and, what is more, a man among men.

Henceforth we live in a new world. The sun does not rise nor set for us as formerly. "Old things have passed away and all things have become new."

I once went abroad among men with all my quills erect. There was cause for it. I always looked for insult and buffetings, and was seldom disappointed in finding them. Now civility is the rule, and insult the exception.

The Curtain Has Lifted

At last, at last, the black man has a future. Heretofore all was dark, mysterious, chaotic. We were chained to all the unutterable horrors of never ending fixedness. Others might improve and make progress, but for us there was nothing but the unending monotony of stagnation, of moral, mental and social death. The curtain is now lifted. The dismal deathcloud of slavery has passed away. Today we are free American citizens. We have ourselves, we have a country, and we have a future in common with other men.

One of the most remarkable features of this grand revolution is its thoroughness. Never was revolution more complete. Nothing has been left for time. No probation has been imposed. The Hebrews tarried in the wilderness forty years before they reached the land of promise. The West India [Caribbean] slaves had their season of apprenticeship. Feudal slavery died a lingering death in Europe. Hayti [Haiti] rose to freedom only by degrees and by limited concessions. Religious liberty as now enjoyed came only in slow installments; but our liberty has come all at once, full and complete. The most

Born into slavery as Frederick Augustus Washington Bailey, Frederick Douglass lived from 1818 to 1895. He was an American abolitionist, editor, orator, author, and diplomat. Public domain.

exacting could not ask more than we have got; the most urgent could not have demanded it more promptly. We have all we asked, and more than we expected. . . .

The Amendment's Importance

But what does this Fifteenth amendment mean to us? I will tell you. It means that the colored people are now and will be held to be, by the whole nation, responsible for their own existence and their well or ill being. It means that we are placed upon an equal footing with all other men, and that the glory or shame of our future is to be wholly our own. For one, I accept this new situation gladly. I do so for myself and I do so for you; and I do so in the full belief that the future will show that we are equal to the responsibility which this great measure has imposed upon us.

What does this measure mean? I will tell you. It means progress, civilization, knowledge, manhood. It means that you and I and all of us shall leave the narrow places in which we now breathe, and live in the same comfort and independence enjoyed by other men. It means industry, application to business, economy in the use of our earnings, and the building up of a solid character—one which will deserve and command the respect of our fellow citizens of all races. It means that color is no longer to be a calamity; that race is to be no longer a crime; and that liberty is to be the right of all.

The black man has no longer an apology for lagging behind in the race of civilization. If he rises the glory is to be his, if he falls the shame will be his. He is to be the architect of his own fortunes. If we are despised, it is because we make ourselves despicable, if we are honored it is because we exhibit qualities deserving of honor. Character, not color, is to be the criterion. A great many of the American people are disturbed about the present state of things. They like a strong government [English writer Thomas] Carlyle says we are rushing to ruin with cataract speed. Others are croakers in the mournful style of [American author Edgar Allan] Poe's raven [known for always saying "never more"]—we shall never again see such days as were the earlier days of our republic, say they— never such statesmen as [Henry] Clay, [John C.] Calhoun, [Daniel] Webster, and others. The two races cannot work well together. However, he would let the croakers croak on. He never felt more hopeful than now, and the croakers do not disturb him. We had them during the war, and we shall continue to have them. During the dark hours of the war, when we needed strong words to hold us up, there were croakers. They said we never would put down rebellion, or abolish slavery, or reconstruct the South, and we have accomplished all. South Carolina has adopted all the amendments.

He [the Black Man] compassionated his Democratic brethren. They are in a state of honest alarm, and we ought to say some word of comfort to them. He would tell his Democratic friends, that Jefferson wrote the Fourteenth Amendment. That amendment is but the carrying out of Democratic doctrine—that all men are created equal, and have the inalienable right to life liberty and the pursuit of happiness. We gave the credit to [William Lloyd] Garrison, [Benjamin] Lundy, and others [who fought for an end to slavery]. When God told the children of Israel to go free, the great truth had its origin.

We are a great nation—not we colored people particularly, but all of us. We are all together now. We are fellow-citizens of a common country. What a country—fortunate in its institutions, in its Fifteenth amendment, in its future. We are made up of a variety of nations—Chinese, Jews, Africans, Europeans, and all sorts. These different races give the Government a powerful arm to defend it. They will vie with each other in hardship and peril, and will be united in defending it from all its enemies, whether from within or without.

The Federal Government Must Enforce the Fifteenth Amendment's Guarantees

Martin Luther King Jr.

The Fifteenth Amendment's voting guarantees faced continual challenges after the amendment was ratified in 1870, and those problems persisted well into the twentieth century. States and localities tried to limit the voting ability of African Americans and others by instituting poll taxes, making it difficult to register, even sometimes with intimidation and violence. Problems were especially dire in the Southern states, where in the late 1800s many localities enacted "Jim Crow" laws that placed whites and African Americans into segregated communities.

The following selection is a speech given by civil rights leader Martin Luther King Jr. in 1957. In it he cites the 1954 Supreme Court decision in Brown v. Board of Education, *which began the end of the Jim Crow laws. King proclaims that American leaders of all origins need to continue the process by making sure that African Americans can fully exercise the Fifteenth Amendment's guarantees. King's subsequent efforts, as well as those of many others, resulted in the passage of a broad, national voting rights bill in 1965.*

Three years ago the Supreme Court of this nation rendered in simple, eloquent, and unequivocal language a decision which will long be stenciled on the mental sheets of succeeding generations. For all men of goodwill, this May seventeenth decision came as a joyous daybreak to end the long night of human captivity. It came as a great beacon light of hope to millions of disinherited people throughout the world who had dared only to dream of freedom.

Martin Luther King Jr. "Give Us the Ballot," MLKonline.net, May 17, 1957. Reproduced by arrangement with the Estate of Martin Luther King Jr., c/o Writers House Inc. as agent for the proprietor New York, NY.

Unfortunately, this noble and sublime decision has not gone without opposition. This opposition has often risen to ominous proportions. Many states have risen up in open defiance. The legislative halls of the South ring loud with such words as "interposition" and "nullification."

But even more, all types of conniving methods are still being used to prevent Negroes from becoming registered voters. The denial of this sacred right is a tragic betrayal of the highest mandates of our democratic tradition. And so our most urgent request to the president of the United States and every member of Congress is to give us the right to vote.

Give us the ballot, and we will no longer have to worry the federal government about our basic rights.

Give us the ballot, and we will no longer plead to the federal government for passage of an anti-lynching law; we will by the power of our vote write the law on the statute books of the South and bring an end to the dastardly acts of the hooded perpetrators of violence.

Give us the ballot, and we will transform the salient misdeeds of bloodthirsty mobs into the calculated good deeds of orderly citizens.

Give us the ballot and we will fill our legislative halls with men of goodwill and send to the sacred halls of Congress men who will not sign a "Southern Manifesto" because of their devotion to the manifesto of justice.

Give us the ballot and we will place judges on the benches of the south who will do justly and love mercy, and we will place at the head of the southern states governors who will, who have felt not only the tang of the human, but the glow of the Divine.

Give us the ballot and we will quietly and nonviolently, without rancor or bitterness, implement the Supreme Court's decision of May seventeenth, 1954.

In 1964, Martin Luther King Jr. became the youngest person to receive the Nobel Peace Prize for his work to end racial segregation and discrimination through nonviolent means. The Library of Congress.

Leadership Is Needed

In this juncture of our nation's history, there is an urgent need for dedicated and courageous leadership. If we are to solve the problems ahead and make racial justice a reality, this leadership must be fourfold.

First, there is need for strong, aggressive leadership from the federal government. So far, only the judicial branch of the government has evinced this quality of leadership. If the executive and legislative branches of the government were as concerned about the protection of our citizenship rights as the federal courts have been, then the transition from a segregated to an integrated society would be infinitely smoother. But we so often look to Washington in vain for this concern. In the midst of the tragic breakdown of law and order, the executive branch of the government is all too silent and apathetic. In the midst of the desperate need for civil rights legislation, the legislative branch of the government is all too stagnant and hypocritical.

This dearth of positive leadership from the federal government is not confined to one particular political party. Both political parties have betrayed the cause of justice. The Democrats have betrayed it by capitulating to the prejudices and undemocratic practices of the southern Dixiecrats. The Republicans have betrayed it by capitulating to the blatant hypocrisy of right wing, reactionary northerners. These men so often have a high blood pressure of words and an anemia of deeds.

In the midst of these prevailing conditions, we come to Washington today pleading with the president and members of Congress to provide a strong, moral, and courageous leadership for a situation that cannot permanently be evaded. We come humbly to say to the men in the forefront of our government that the civil rights issue is not an Ephemeral, evanescent domestic issue that can be kicked about by reactionary guardians of the status quo; it is rather an eternal moral issue which may well determine the destiny of our nation in the ideological struggle with communism. The hour is late. The clock of destiny is ticking out. We must act now, before it is too late.

A second area in which there is need for strong leadership is from the white northern liberals. There is a dire need today for a liberalism which is truly liberal. What we are witnessing today in so many northern communities is a sort of quasi-liberalism which is based on the principle of looking sympathetically at all sides. It is a liberalism so bent on seeing all sides, that it fails to become committed to either side. It is a liberalism that is so objectively analytical that it is not subjectively committed. It is a liberalism which is neither hot nor cold, but lukewarm. We call for a liberalism from the North which will be thoroughly committed to the ideal of racial justice and will not be deterred by the propaganda and subtle words of those who say: "Slow up for a while; you're pushing too fast."

A third source that we must look to for strong leadership is from the moderates of the white South. It is unfortunate that at this time the leadership of the white South stems from the close-minded reactionaries. These persons gain prominence and power by the dissemination of false ideas and by deliberately appealing to the deepest hate responses within the human mind. It is my firm belief that this close-minded, reactionary, recalcitrant group constitutes a numerical minority. There are in the white South more open-minded moderates than appears on the surface. These persons are silent today because of fear of social, political, and economic reprisals. God grant that the white moderates of the South will rise up courageously, without fear, and take up the leadership in this tense period of transition.

I cannot close without stressing the urgent need for strong, courageous and intelligent leadership from the Negro community. We need a leadership that is calm and yet positive. This is no day for the rabble-rouser, whether he be Negro or white. We must realize that we are grappling with the most weighty social problem of this nation, and in grappling with such a complex problem there is no place for misguided emotionalism. We must work passionately and unrelentingly for the goal of freedom, but we must be sure that our hands are clean in the struggle. We must never struggle with falsehood, hate, or malice. We must never become bitter. I know how we feel sometime. There is the danger that those of us who have been forced so long to stand amid the tragic midnight of oppression—those of us who have been trampled over, those of us who have been kicked about—there is the danger that we will become bitter. But if we will become bitter and indulge in hate campaigns, the new order which is emerging will be nothing but a duplication of the old order.

We must meet hate with love. We must meet physical force with soul force. There is still a voice crying out through the vista of time, saying: "Love your enemies bless them that curse you pray for them that despitefully use you." Then, and only then, can you matriculate into the university of eternal life. That same voice cries out in terms lifted to cosmic proportions: "He who lives by the sword will perish by the sword." And history is replete with the bleached bones of nations that failed to follow this command. We must follow nonviolence and love.

Now, I'm not talking about a sentimental, shallow kind of love. I'm not talking about *eros*, which is a sort of aesthetic, romantic love. I'm not even talking about *philia* which is a sort of intimate affection between personal friends. But I'm talking about *agape*. I'm talking about the love of God in the hearts of men. I'm talking about a type of love which will cause you to love the person who does the evil deed while hating the deed that the person does. We've got to love.

Gracious Victory

There is another warning signal. We talk a great deal about our rights, and rightly so. We proudly proclaim that three-fourths of the peoples of the world are colored. We have the privilege of noticing in our generation the great drama of freedom and independence as it unfolds in Asia and Africa. All of these things are in line with the unfolding work of Providence. But we must be sure that we accept them in the right spirit. We must not seek to use our emerging freedom and our growing power to do the same thing to the white minority that has been done to us for so many centuries. Our aim must never be to defeat or humiliate the white man. We must not become victimized with a philosophy of black supremacy. God is not interested merely in freeing black men and brown men and yellow men, but God is interested in freeing the whole human race. We must work with determination to create a society, not where black men are superior and other men are inferior and vice versa, but a society in which all men will live together as brothers and respect the dignity and worth of human personality.

We must also avoid the temptation of being victimized with a psychology of victors. We have won marvelous victories. Through the work of the NAACP [National Association for the Advancement of Colored People] we have been able to do some of the most amazing things of this generation. And I come this afternoon with nothing but praise for this great organization, the work that it has already done and the work that it will do in the future. And although they're outlawed in Alabama and other states, the fact still remains that this organization has done more to achieve civil rights for Negroes than any other organization we can point to. Certainly, this is fine.

But we must not, however, remain satisfied with a court victory over our white brothers. We must respond to every decision with an understanding of those who have opposed us and with an appreciation of the difficult adjustments that the court orders pose for them. We must act in such a way as to make possible a coming together of white people and colored people on the basis of a real harmony of interest and understanding. We must seek an integration based on mutual respect.

I conclude by saying that each of us must keep faith in the future. Let us not despair. Let us realize that as we struggle for justice and freedom, we have cosmic companionship. This is the long faith of the Hebraic-Christian tradition: that God is not some Aristotelian Unmoved Mover who merely contemplates upon himself. He is not merely a self-knowing God, but an other-loving God forever working through history for the establishment of His kingdom.

And those of us who call [on] the name of Jesus Christ find something of an event in our Christian faith that tells us this. There is something in our faith that says to us, "Never despair; never give up; never feel that the cause of righteousness and justice is doomed." There is something in our Christian faith, at the center of it, which says to us that Good Friday may occupy the throne for a day, but ultimately it must give way to the triumphant beat of the drums of Easter. There is something in our faith that says evil may so shape events that Caesar will occupy the palace and Christ the cross but one day that same Christ will rise up and split history into a.d. and b.c., so that even the name, the life of Caesar must be dated by his name. There is something in this universe which justifies Carlyle in saying: "No lie can live forever." There is something in this universe which justifies [American jurist] William Cullen Bryant in saying: "Truth crushed to earth will rise again." There is something in this universe which justifies [American poet] James Russell Lowell in saying:

Truth forever on the scaffold,

Wrong forever on the throne.

Yet that scaffold sways the future,

And behind the dim unknown

Stands God within the shadow,

Keeping watch above His own.

Go out with that faith today. Go back to your homes in the Southland to that faith, with that faith today. Go back to Philadelphia, to New York, to Detroit and Chicago with that faith today: that the universe is on our side in the struggle. Stand up for justice. Sometimes it gets hard, but it is always difficult to get out of Egypt, for the Red Sea always stands before you with discouraging dimensions. And even after you've crossed the Red Sea, you have to move through a wilderness with prodigious hilltops of evil and gigantic mountains of opposition. But I say to you this afternoon: Keep moving. Let nothing slow you up. Move on with dignity and honor and respectability.

I realize that it will cause restless nights sometimes. It might cause losing a job; it will cause suffering and sacrifice. It might even cause physical death for some. But if physical death is the price that some must pay to free their children from a permanent life of psychological death then nothing can be more Christian. Keep going today. Keep moving amid every obstacle. Keep moving amid every mountain of opposition. If you will do that with dignity when the history books are written in the future, the historians will have to look back and say, "There lived a great people. A people with 'fleecy locks and black complexion,' but a people who injected new meaning into the veins of civilization; a people which stood up with dignity and honor and saved Western civilization in her darkest hour; a people that gave new integrity and a new dimension of love to our civilization." When that happens, "the morning stars will sing together, and the sons of God will shout for joy."

CONSTITUTIONAL
AMENDMENTS
BEYOND THE BILL OF RIGHTS

CHAPTER 2

Challenging and Affirming the Fifteenth Amendment

Individual States Cannot Restrict the Fifteenth Amendment's Guarantees

Edward D. White

In 1907, the Oklahoma Territory, which included certain Indian Territories, was given statehood, making Oklahoma the forty-sixth state in the union. Its state constitution was enacted in 1910, but it contained provisions that tried to limit voting rights by imposing a literacy test. The constitution also asserted that persons who had the right to vote "under any form of government" on or before January 1, 1866, or the descendants of such persons, would not be subject to the literacy requirement.

These provisions were challenged by those who asserted that the provision violated the Fifteenth Amendment by putting in place requirements that predated the amendment. The case of Guinn v. United States *reached the U.S. Supreme Court in 1913, and the Court delivered its verdict in 1915. In the majority opinion written by Chief Justice Edward D. White, the Court asserted that Oklahoma did not have the right to "grandfather" in voting regulations that might limit the Fifteenth Amendment's guarantees and declared the provisions unconstitutional. The year 1866 was significant in that few African Americans could vote anywhere before then. Had Oklahoma's provisions been allowed to stand, any African American voters in the state would have had to fulfill the literacy requirements.*

Edward D. White served the nation as chief justice from 1910 to 1921.

This case is before us on a certificate drawn by the court below as the basis of two questions which are submitted for our solution in order to enable the court correctly to de-

Edward D. White, "*Guinn v. U.S.*, 238 U.S. 347 (1915)," U.S. Supreme Court, June 21, 1915. Reproduced by permission.

cide issues in a case which it has under consideration. Those issues arose from an indictment and conviction of certain election officers of the state of Oklahoma (the plaintiffs in error) of the crime of having conspired unlawfully, wilfully, and fraudulently to deprive certain negro citizens, on account of their race and color, of a right to vote at a general election held in that state in 1910, they being entitled to vote under the state law, and which right was secured to them by the 15th Amendment to the Constitution of the United States. The prosecution was directly concerned with 5508, Revised Statutes, now 19 of the Penal Code which is as follows:

'If two or more persons conspire to injure, oppress, threaten, or intimidate any citizen in the free exercise or enjoyment of any right or privilege secured to him by the Constitution or laws of the United States, or because of his having so exercised the same; or if two or more persons go in disguise on the highway, or on the premises of another, with intent to prevent or hinder his free exercise or enjoyment of any right or privilege so secured, they shall be fined not more than five thousand dollars and imprisoned not more than ten years, and shall, moreover, be thereafter ineligible to any office, or place of honor, profit, or trust created by the Constitution or laws of the United States.' We concentrate and state from the certificate only matters which we deem essential to dispose of the questions asked.

Suffrage in Oklahoma was regulated by 4a, article 3, of the Constitution under which the state was admitted into the Union. Shortly after the admission there was submitted an amendment to the Constitution making a radical change in that article, which was adopted prior to November 8, 1910. At an election for members of Congress which followed the adoption of this amendment, certain election officers, in enforcing its provisions, refused to allow certain negro citizens to vote who were clearly entitled to vote under the provision of the Constitution under which the state was admitted; that is, before the amendment; and who, it is equally clear, were not entitled to vote under the provision of the suffrage amendment if that amendment governed. The persons so excluded based their claim of right to vote upon the original Constitution and upon the assertion that the suffrage amendment was void because in conflict with the prohibitions of the 15th Amendment, and therefore afforded no basis for denying them the right guaranteed and protected by that Amendment. And upon the assumption that this claim was justified and that the election officers had violated the 15th Amendment in denying the right to vote, this prosecution, as we have said, was commenced. At the trial the court instructed that by the 15th Amendment the states were prohibited from discriminating as to suffrage because of race, color, or previous condition of servitude, and that Congress, in pursuance of the authority which was conferred upon it by the very terms of the Amendment, to enforce its provisions had enacted the following:

'All citizens of the United States who are otherwise qualified by law to vote at any election by the people in any state, territory, district, . . . municipality, or other territorial subdivision, shall be entitled and allowed to vote at all such elections without distinction of race, color, or previous condition of servitude; any constitution, law, custom, or usage, or regulation of any state or territory, or by or under its authority, to the contrary notwithstanding.'

It then instructed as follows:

'The state amendment which imposes the test of reading and writing any section of the state Constitution as a condition to voting to persons not, on or prior to January 1, 1866, entitled to vote under some form of government, or then residents in some foreign nation, or a lineal descendant of such person, is not valid, but you may consider it in so far as it was in good faith relied and acted upon by the defendants in ascertaining their intent and motive. If you believe from the evidence that the defendants formed a common design and cooperated in denying the colored voters of Union township precinct, or any of them, entitled to vote, the privilege of voting, but this was due to a mistaken belief sincerely entertained by the defendants as to the qualifications of the voters,—that is, if the motive actuating the defendants was honest, and they simply erred in the conception of their duty,—then the criminal intent requisite to their guilt is wanting and they cannot be convicted. On the other hand, if they knew or believed these colored persons were entitled to vote, and their purpose was to unfairly and fraudulently deny the right of suffrage to them, or any of them entitled thereto, on account of their race and color, then their purpose was a corrupt one, and they cannot be shielded by their official positions.'

Questions Before the Court

The questions which the court below asks are these:

1. 'Was the amendment to the Constitution of Oklahoma, heretofore set forth, valid?

2. 'Was that amendment void in so far as it attempted to debar from the right or privilege of voting for a qualified candidate for a member of Congress in Oklahoma unless they were able to read and write any section of the Constitution of Oklahoma, negro citizens of the United States who were otherwise qualified to vote for a qualified candidate for a member of Congress in that state, but who were not, and none of whose lineal ancesters was, entitled to vote under any form of government on January 1, 1866, or at any time prior thereto, because they were then slaves?'

As these questions obviously relate to the provisions concerning suffrage in the original Constitution and the amendment to those provisions which form the basis of the controversy, we state the text of both. The original clause, so far as material, was this:

'The qualified electors of the state shall be male citizens of the United States, male citizens of the state, and male persons of Indian descent native of the United States, who are over the age of twenty-one years, who have resided in the state one year, in the county six months, and in the election precinct thirty days, next preceding the election at which any such elector offers to vote.'

And this is the amendment:

'No person shall be registered as an elector of this state or be allowed to vote in any election held herein, unless he be able to read and write any section of the Constitution of the state of Oklahoma; but no person who was, on January 1st, 1866, or any time prior thereto, entitled to vote under any form of government, or who at that time resided in some foreign nation, and no lineal descendant of such person, shall be denied the right to register and vote because of his inability to so read and write sections of such Constitution. Precinct election inspectors having in charge the registration of electors shall enforce the provisions of this section at the time of registration, provided registration be required. Should registration be dispensed with, the provisions of this section shall be enforced by the precinct election officers when electors apply for ballots to vote.'

Considering the questions in the light of the text of the suffrage amendment it is apparent that they are twofold because of the twofold character of the provisions as to suffrage which the amendment contains. The first question is concerned with that provision of the amendment which fixes a standard by which the right to vote is given upon conditions existing on January 1, 1866, and relieves those coming within that standard from the standard based on a literacy test which is established by the other provision of the amendment. The second question asks as to the validity of the literacy test and how far, if intrinsically valid, it would continue to exist and be

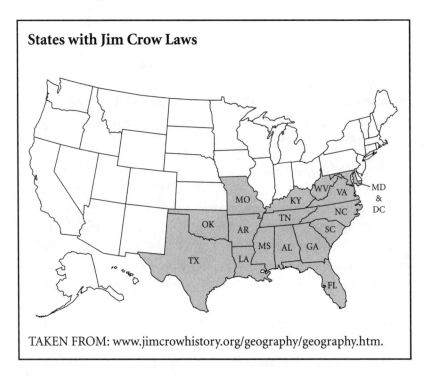

States with Jim Crow Laws

TAKEN FROM: www.jimcrowhistory.org/geography/geography.htm.

operative in the event the standard based upon January 1, 1866, should be held to be illegal as violative of the 15th Amendment.

Unreasonable Standards

To avoid that which is unnecessary let us at once consider and sift the propositions of the United States on the one hand, and of the plaintiffs in error, on the other, in order to reach with precision the real and final question to be considered. The United States insists that the provision of the amendment which fixes a standard based upon January 1, 1866, is repugnant to the prohibitions of the 15th Amendment because in substance and effect that provision, if not an express, is certainly an open, repudiation of the 15th Amendment, and hence the provision in question was stricken with nullity in its inception by the self-operative force of the Amendment, and, as the result of the same power, was at all subsequent times devoid of any vitality whatever.

For the plaintiffs in error, on the other hand, it is said the states have the power to fix standards for suffrage, and that power was not taken away by the 15th Amendment, but only limited to the extent of the prohibitions which that Amendment established. This being true, as the standard fixed does not in terms make any discrimination on account of race, color, or previous condition of servitude, since all, whether negro or white, who come within its requirements, enjoy the privilege of voting, there is no ground upon which to rest the contention that the provision violates the 15th Amendment. This, it is insisted, must be the case unless it is intended to expressly deny the state's right to provide a standard for suffrage, or what is equivalent thereto, to assert: (a) that the judgment of the state, exercised in the exertion of that power, is subject to Federal judicial review or supervision, or (b) that it may be questioned and be brought within the prohibitions of the Amendment by attributing to the legislative authority an occult motive to violate the Amendment, or by assuming that an exercise of the otherwise lawful power may be invalidated because of conclusions concerning its operation in practical execution and resulting discrimination was arising therefrom, albeit such discrimination was not expressed in the standard fixed, or fairly to be implied, but simply arose from inequalities naturally inhering in those who must come within the standard in order to enjoy the right to vote.

On the other hand, the United States denies the relevancy of these contentions. It says state power to provide for suffrage is not disputed, although, of course, the authority of the 15th Amendment and the limit on that power which it imposes is insisted upon. Hence, no assertion denying the right of a state to exert judgment and discretion in fixing the qualification of suffrage is advanced, and no right to question the motive of the state in establishing a standard as to such subjects under such circumstances, or to review or supervise the same, is relied upon, and no power to destroy an otherwise valid exertion of authority upon the mere ultimate operation of the power exercised is asserted. And applying these principles to the very case in hand, the argument of the government in substance says: No question is raised by the government concerning the validity of the literacy test provided for in the amendment under consideration as an independent standard since the conclusion is plain that that test rests on the exercise of state judgment, and therefore cannot be here assailed either by disregarding the state's power to judge on the subject, or by testing its motive in enacting the provision. The real question involved, so the argument of the government insists, is the repugnancy of the standard which the amendment makes, based upon the conditions existing on January 1st, 1866, because on its face and inherently considering the substance of things, that standard is a mere denial of the restrictions imposed by the prohibitions of the 15th Amendment, and by necessary result re-creates and perpetuates the very conditions which the Amendment was intended to destroy. From this it is urged that no legitimate discretion could have entered into the fixing of such standard which involved only the determination to directly set at naught or by indirection avoid the commands of the Amendment. And it is insisted that nothing contrary to these propositions is involved in the contention of the government that if the standard which the suffrage amendment fixes, based upon the conditions existing on January 1, 1866, be found to be void for the reasons urged, the other and literacy test is also void, since that contention rests not upon any assertion on the part of the government of any abstract repugnancy of the literacy test to the prohibitions of the 15th Amendment, but upon the relation between that test and the other, as formulated in the suffrage amendment, and the inevitable result which it is deemed must follow from holding it to be void if the other is so declared to be.

Looking comprehensively at these contentions of the parties it plainly results that the conflict between them is much narrower than it would seem to be because the premise which the arguments of the plaintiffs in error attribute to the propositions of the United States is by it denied. On the very face of things it is clear that the United States disclaims the gloss put upon its contentions by limiting them to the propositions which we have hitherto pointed out, since it rests the contentions which it makes as to the assailed provision of the suffrage amendment solely upon the ground that it involves an unmistakable, although it may be a somewhat disguised, refusal to give effect to the prohibitions of the 15th Amendment by creating a standard which, it is repeated, but calls to life the very conditions which that Amendment was adopted to destroy and which it had destroyed.

The questions then are: (1) Giving to the propositions of the government the interpretation which the government puts upon them, and assuming that the suffrage provision has the significance which the government assumes it to have, is that provision as a matter of law repugnant to the 15th Amendment? Which leads us, of course, to consider the operation and effect of the 15th Amendment. (2) If yes, has the assailed amendment in so far as it fixes a standard for voting as of January 1, 1866, the meaning which the government attributes to it? Which leads us to analyze and interpret that provision of the amendment. (3) If the investigation as to the two prior subjects establishes that the standard fixed as of January 1, 1866, is void, what, if any, effect does that conclusion have upon the literacy standard otherwise established by the amendment? Which involves determining whether that standard, if legal, may survive the recognition of the fact that the other, or 1866, standard, has not and never had any legal existence. Let us consider these subjects under separate headings.

Details of the Fifteenth Amendment

1. The operation and effect of the 15th Amendment. This is its text: Section 1. The right of citizens of the United States to vote shall not be denied or abridged by the United States or by any state on account of race, color, or previous condition of servitude.

'Section 2. The Congress shall have power to enforce this article by appropriate legislation.'

(a) Beyond doubt the Amendment does not take away from the state governments in a general sense the power over suffrage which has belonged to those governments from the beginning, and without the possession of which power the whole fabric upon which the division of state and national authority under the Constitution and the organization of both governments rest would be without support, and both the authority of the nation and the state would fall to the ground. In fact, the very command of the Amendment recognizes the possession of the general power by the state, since the Amendment seeks to regulate its exercise as to the particular subject with which it deals.

(b) But it is equally beyond the possibility of question that the Amendment in express terms restricts the power of the United States or the states to abridge or deny the right of a citizen of the United States to vote on account of race, color, or previous condition of servitude. The restriction is coincident with the power and prevents its exertion in disregard to the command of the Amendment. But while this is true, it is true also that the Amendment does not change, modify, or deprive the states of their full power as to suffrage except, of course, as to the subject with which the Amendment deals and to the extent that obedience to its command is necessary. Thus the authority over suffrage which the states possess and the limitation which the Amendment imposes are co-ordinate and one may not destroy the other without bringing about the destruction of both.

(c) While in the true sense, therefore, the Amendment gives no right of suffrage, it was long ago recognized that in operation its prohibition might measurably have that effect; that is to say, that as the command of the Amendment was self-executing and reached without legislative action the conditions of discrimination against which it was aimed, the result might arise that, as a consequence of the striking down of a discrimination clause, a right of suffrage would be enjoyed by reason of the generic character of the provision which would remain after the discrimination was stricken out. A familiar illustration of this doctrine resulted from the effect of the adoption of the Amendment on state Constitutions in which, at the time of the adoption of the Amendment, the right of suffrage was conferred on all white male citizens, since by the inherent power of the Amendment the word 'white' disappeared and therefore all male citizens, without discrimination on account of race, color, or previous condition of servitude, came under the generic grant of suffrage made by the state.

With these principles before us how can there be room for any serious dispute concerning the repugnancy of the standard based upon January 1, 1866 (a date which preceded the adoption of the 15th Amendment), if the suffrage provision fixing that standard is susceptible of the significance which the government attributes to it? Indeed, there seems no escape from the conclusion that to hold that there was even possibility for dispute on the subject would be but to declare that the 15th Amendment not only had not the self-executing power which it has been recognized to have from the beginning, but that its provisions were wholly inoperative because susceptible of being rendered inapplicable by mere forms of expression embodying no exercise of judgment and resting upon no discernible reason other than the purpose to disregard the prohibitions of the Amendment by creating a standard of voting which, on its face, was in substance but a revitalization of conditions which, when they prevailed in the past, had been destroyed by the self-operative force of the Amendment.

States May Restrict Nonwhites from Voting in State Primaries

Owen Roberts

While the Fifteenth Amendment guaranteed the right to vote for all citizens regardless of skin color or ethnic background, it did not end the ability of individual states to enact their own voting rules. Many states used those rules to find ways to restrict voters. In Texas, only whites were permitted to take part in the states' Democratic Party primaries in the first decades of the twentieth century. When an African American resident of Houston, R.R. Grovey, challenged these rules on the grounds that he was a full member of the Democratic Party, the case went all the way to the U.S. Supreme Court.

In 1935 the Court decided unanimously that the Texas Democratic Party did indeed have the right to limit voting to white members. The Court's main line of reasoning was that the party was a voluntary organization and therefore not subject to the same laws that govern states.

The petitioner, by complaint filed in the justice court of Harris County, Tex., alleged that although he is a citizen of the United States and of the state and county, and a member of and believer in the tenets of the Democratic Party, the respondent, the county clerk, a state officer, having as such only public functions to perform, refused him a ballot for a Democratic Party primary election, because he is of the negro race. He demanded ten dollars damages. The pleading quotes articles of the Revised Civil Statutes of Texas which require the nomination of candidates at primary elections by any organized political party whose nominees received 100,000 votes or more at the preceding general election, and recites that

Owen Roberts, "*Grovey v. Townsend*, 295 U.S. 45 (1935)," U.S. Supreme Court, April 1, 1935. Reproduced by permission.

agreeably to these enactments a Democratic primary election was held on July 28, 1934, at which petitioner had the right to vote. Referring to statutes which regulate absentee voting at primary elections, the complaint states the petitioner expected to be absent from the county on the date of the primary election, and demanded of the respondent an absentee ballot, which was refused him in virtue of a resolution of the state Democratic Convention of Texas, adopted May 24, 1932, which is:

> 'Be it resolved, that all white citizens of the State of Texas who are qualified to vote under the Constitution and laws of the state shall be eligible to membership in the Democratic party and as such entitled to participate in its deliberations.'

The complaint charges that the respondent acted without legal excuse and his wrongful and unlawful acts constituted a violation of the Fourteenth and Fifteenth Amendments of the Federal Constitution.

A demurrer [exception], assigning as reasons that the complaint was insufficient in law and stated no cause of action, was sustained; and a motion for a new trial, reasserting violation of the federal rights mentioned in the complaint, was overruled. We granted certiorari [an approval raising the case from lower courts to the Supreme Court], because of the importance of the federal question presented, which has not been determined by this court. Our jurisdiction is clear, as the justice court is the highest state court in which a decision may be had, and the validity of the Constitution and statutes of the state was drawn in question on the ground of their being repugnant to the Constitution of the United States. The charge is that respondent, a state officer, in refusing to furnish petitioner a ballot, obeyed the law of Texas, and the consequent denial of petitioner's right to vote in the primary election because of his race and color was state action forbidden by the Federal Constitution; and it is claimed that former decisions require us so to hold. The cited cases are, however, not in point. In *Nixon v. Herndon* [1927], a statute which enacted that 'in no event shall a negro be eligible to participate in a Democratic party primary election held in the State of Texas,' was pronounced offensive to the Fourteenth Amendment. In *Nixon v. Condon* [1932], a statute was drawn in question which provided that 'every political party in this State through its State Executive Committee shall have the power to prescribe the qualifications of its own members and shall in its own way determine who shall be qualified to vote or otherwise participate in such political party.' We held this was a delegation of state power to the state executive committee and made its determination conclusive irrespective of any expression of the party's will by its convention, and therefore the committee's action barring negroes from the party primaries was state action prohibited by the Fourteenth Amendment. Here the qualifications of citizens to participate in party counsels and to vote at party primaries have been declared by the representatives of the party in convention assembled, and this action upon its face is not state action. The question whether under the Constitution and laws of Texas such a declaration as to party membership amounts to state action was expressly reserved in *Nixon v. Condon*. Petitioner insists that for various reasons the resolution of the state convention limiting membership in the Democratic Party in Texas to white voters does not relieve the exclusion of negroes from participation in Democratic primary elections of its true nature as the act of the state. First. An argument pressed upon us in *Nixon v. Condon*, which we found it unnecessary to consider, is again presented. It is that the primary election was held under statutory compulsion; is wholly statutory in origin and incidents; those charged with its management have been deprived by statute and judicial decision of all power to establish qualifications for participation therein inconsistent with those laid down by the laws of the state, save only that the managers of such elections have been given the power to deny negroes the vote. It is further urged that while the election is designated that of the Democratic Party, the statutes not only require this method of selecting party nominees, but define the powers and duties of the party's representatives and of those who are to conduct the election so completely, and make them so thoroughly officers of the state, that any action taken by them in connection with the qualifications of members of the party is in fact state action and not party action.

State Election Rules

In support of this view petitioner refers to title 50 of the Revised Civil Statutes of Texas of 1925, which by article 3101 requires that any party whose members cast more than 100,000 ballots at the previous election shall nominate candidates through primaries, and fixes the date at which they are to be held; by article 2939 requires primary election officials to be qualified voters; by article 2955 declares the same qualifications for voting in such an election as in the general elections; by article 2956, permits absentee voting as in a general election; by article 2978 requires that only an official ballot shall be used, as in a general election; by articles 2980, 2981 specifies the form of ballot and how it shall be marked, as other sections do for general elections; by article 2984 fixes the number of ballots to be provided, as another article does for general elections; by articles 2986, 2987, and 2990 permits the use of voting booths, guard rails, and ballot boxes which by other statutes are provided for general elections; by articles 2998 and 3104 requires the officials of primary elections to take the same oath as officials at the general elections; by article 3002 defines the powers of judges at primary elections; by articles 3003–3025 provides elaborately for the purity of the ballot box; by article 3028 commands that the sealed ballot boxes be delivered to the county clerk after the election, as is provided by another article for the general election; and by article 3041 confers jurisdiction of election contests upon district courts, as is done by another article with respect to general elections. A perusal of these provisions so it is said will convince that the state has prescribed and regulated party primaries as fully as general elections, and has made those who manage the primaries state officers subject to state direction and control.

While it is true that Texas has by its laws elaborately provided for the expression of party preference as to nominees, has required that preference to be expressed in a certain form of voting, and has attempted in minute detail to protect the suffrage of the members of the organization against fraud, it is equally true that the primary is a party primary; the expenses of it are not borne by the state, but by members of the party seeking nomination and article 3116, as amended by Acts 1927, c. 54, 1; the ballots are furnished not by the state, but by the agencies of the party; the votes are counted and the returns made by instrumentalities created by the party; and the state recognizes the state convention as the organ of the party for the declaration of principles and the formulation of policies. . . .

After referring to article 3107, as amended by Acts 1927, which limits the power of the state executive committee of a party to determine who shall be qualified to vote at primary elections, the court said:

'The committee's discretionary power is further restricted by the statute directing that a single, uniform pledge be required of the primary participants. The effect of the statutes is to decline to give recognition to the lodgment of power in a State Executive Committee, to be exercised at its discretion.'

Although it did not pass upon the constitutionality of section 3107, as we did in *Nixon v. Condon*, the Court thus recognized the fact upon which our decision turned, that the effort was to vest in the state executive committee the power to bind the party by its decision as to who might be admitted to membership.

In *Bell v. Hill* [1934], the same court, in a mandamus ["we order"] proceeding instituted after the adoption by the state convention of the resolution of May 24, 1932, restricting eligibility for membership in the Democratic Party to white persons, held the resolution valid and effective. After a full consideration of the nature of political parties in the United States, the court concluded that such parties in the state of Texas arise from the exercise of the free will and liberty of the citizens composing them; that they are voluntary associations for political action, and are not the creatures of the state; and further decided that sections 2 and 27 of article 1 of the state Constitution guaranteed to citizens the liberty of forming political associations, and the only limitation upon this right to be found in that instrument is the clause which requires the maintenance of a republican form of government. The statutes regulating the nomination of candidates by primaries were related by the court to the police power, but were held not to extend to the denial of the right of citizens to form a political party and to determine who might associate with them as members thereof. The court declared that a proper view of the election laws of Texas, and their history, required the conclusion that the Democratic Party in that state is a voluntary political association and, by its representatives assembled in convention, has the power to determine who shall be eligible for membership and, as such, eligible to participate in the party's primaries.

Party Can Determine Membership

We cannot, as petitioner urges, give weight to earlier expressions of the state courts said to be inconsistent with this declaration of the law. The Supreme Court of the state has decided, in a case definitely involving the point, that the

Legislature of Texas has not essayed to interfere, and indeed may not interfere, with the constitutional liberty of citizens to organize a party and to determine the qualifications of its members. If in the past the Legislature has attempted to infringe that right and such infringement has not been gainsaid by the courts, the fact constitutes no reason for our disregarding the considered decision of the state's highest court. The legislative assembly of the state, so far as we are advised, has never attempted to prescribe or to limit the membership of a political party, and it is now settled that it has no power so to do. The state, as its highest tribunal holds, though it has guaranteed the liberty to organize political parties, may legislate for their governance when formed, and for the method whereby they may nominate candidates, but must do so with full recognition of the right of the party to exist, to define its membership, and to adopt such policies as to it shall seem wise. In the light of the principles so announced, we are unable to characterize the managers of the primary election as state officers in such sense that any action taken by them in obedience to the mandate of the state convention respecting eligibility to participate in the organization's deliberations, is state action.

Second. We are told that sections 2 and 27 of the Bill of Rights of the Constitution of Texas as construed in *Bell v. Hill*, violate the Federal Constitution, for the reason that so construed they fail to forbid a classification based upon race and color, whereas in *Love v. Wilcox*, they were not held to forbid classifications based upon party affiliations and membership or nonmembership in organizations other than political parties, which classifications were by article 3107 of Revised Civil Statutes, 1925, as amended, prohibited. But, as above said, in *Love v. Wilcox* the court did not construe or apply any constitutional provision and expressly reserved the question as to the power of a party in convention assembled to specify the qualications for membership therein.

Third. An alternative contention of petitioner is that the state Democratic Convention which adopted the resolution here involved was a mere creature of the state and could not lawfully do what the Federal Constitution prohibits to its creator. The argument is based upon the fact that article 3167 of the Revised Civil Statutes of Texas, 1925, requires a political party desiring to elect delegates to a national convention to hold a state convention on the fourth Tuesday of May, 1928, and every four years thereafter; and provides for the election of delegates to that convention at primary conventions, the procedure of which is regulated by law. In *Bell v. Hill*, the Supreme Court of Texas held that article 3167 does not prohibit declarations of policy by a state Democratic Convention called for the purpose of electing delegates to a national convention. While it may be, as petitioner contends, that we are not bound by the state court's decision on the point, it is entitled to the highest respect, and petitioner points to nothing which in any wise impugns its accuracy. If, as seems to be conceded, the Democratic Party in Texas held conventions many years before the adoption of article 3167, nothing is shown to indicate that the regulation of the method of choosing delegates or fixing the times of their meetings was intended to take away the plenary power of conventions in respect of matters as to which they would normally announce the party's will. Compare *Nixon v. Condon*. We are not prepared to hold that in Texas the state convention of a party has become a mere instrumentality or agency for expressing the voice or will of the state.

Fourth. The complaint states that candidates for the offices of Senator and Representative in Congress were to be nominated at the primary election of July 9, 1934, and that in Texas nomination by the Democratic Party is equivalent to election. These facts (the truth of which the demurrer assumes) the petitioner insists, without more, make out a forbidden discrimination. A similar situation may exist in other states where one or another party includes a great majority of the qualified electors. The argument is that as a negro may not be denied a ballot at a general election on account of his race or color, if exclusion from the primary renders his vote at the general election insignificant and useless, the result is to deny him the suffrage altogether. So to say is to confuse the privilege of membership in a party with the right to vote for one who is to hold a public office. With the former the state need have no concern, with the latter it is bound to concern itself, for the general election is a function of the state government and discrimination by the state as respects participation by negroes on account of their race or color is prohibited by the Federal Constitution.

Fifth. The complaint charges that the Democratic Party has never declared a purpose to exclude negroes. The premise upon which this conclusion rests is that the party is not a state body but a national organization, whose representative is the national Democratic Convention. No such convention, so it is said, has resolved to exclude negroes from membership. We have no occasion to determine the correctness of the position, since even if true it does not tend to prove that the petitioner was discriminated against or denied any right to vote by the state of Texas. Indeed the contention contradicts any such conclusion, for it assumes merely that a state convention, the representative and agent of a state association, has usurped the rightful authority of a national convention which represents a larger and superior country-wide association.

We find no ground for holding that the respondent has in obedience to the mandate of the law of Texas discriminated against the petitioner or denied him any right guaranteed by the Fourteenth and Fifteenth Amendments.

Judgment affirmed.

States Cannot Restrict Voting in Primaries to Whites Only

Stanley F. Reed

In 1935's Grovey v. Townsend, *the Supreme Court decided unanimously that the State of Texas had the right to limit voting in state primaries to white people who had active membership in one of the states' political parties. In 1944's* Smith v. Allwright, *the Court reversed that decision.*

In the majority opinion, written by Stanley F. Reed, the Court asserted that primaries are an essential part of the elective process since, among other factors, they select candidates for office, including such national offices as congressman, senator, and president. Any state rules preventing African Americans from voting in primaries is therefore a violation of the Fifteenth Amendment's guarantees.

This writ of certiorari [request for Supreme Court review] brings here for review a claim for damages in the sum of $5,000 on the part of petitioner, a Negro citizen of the 48th precinct of Harris County, Texas, for the refusal of respondents, election and associate election judges respectively of that precinct, to give petitioner a ballot or to permit him to cast a ballot in the primary election of July 27, 1940, for the nomination of Democratic candidates for the United States Senate and House of Representatives, and Governor and other state officers. The refusal is alleged to have been solely because of the race and color of the proposed voter.

The actions of respondents are said to violate Sections 31 and 43 of Title 81 of the United States Code, 8 U.S.C.A. 31 and 43, in that petitioner was deprived of rights secured by

Stanley F. Reed, "*Smith v. Allwright,* 321 U.S. 649 (1944)," U.S. Supreme Court, April 3, 1944. Reproduced by permission.

Sections 2 and 4 of Article 12 and the Fourteenth, Fifteenth and Seventeenth Amendments to the United States Constitution. . . .

The State of Texas by its Constitution and statutes provides that every person, if certain other requirements are met which are not here in issue, qualified by residence in the district or county 'shall be deemed a qualified elector.' Primary elections for United States Senators, Congressmen and state officers are provided for by Chapters Twelve and Thirteen of the statutes. Under these chapters, the Democratic Party was required to hold the primary which was the occasion of the alleged wrong to petitioner. A summary of the state statutes regulating primaries appears in the footnote. These nominations are to be made by the qualified voters of the party. The Democratic Party of Texas is held by the Supreme Court of that state to be a 'voluntary association,' protected by Section 27 of the Bill of Rights, Art. 1, Constitution of Texas, from interference by the state except that:

'In the interest of fair methods and a fair expression by their members of their preferences in the selection of their nominees, the State may regulate such elections by proper laws.' That court stated further:

'Since the right to organize and maintain a political party is one guaranteed by the Bill of Rights of this state, it necessarily follows that every privilege essential or reasonably appropriate to the exercise of that right is likewise guaranteed, including, of course, the privilege of determining the policies of the party and its membership. Without the privilege of determining the policy of a political association and its membership, the right to organize such an association would be a mere mockery. We think these rights, that is, the right to determine the membership of a political party and to determine its policies, of necessity are to be exercised by the State Convention of such party, and cannot, under any circumstances, be conferred upon a state or governmental agency.'

The Democratic party on May 24, 1932, in a State Convention adopted the following resolution, which has not since been 'amended, abrogated, annulled or voided':

'Be it resolved that all white citizens of the State of Texas who are qualified to vote under the Constitution and laws of the State shall be eligible to membership in the Democratic party and, as such, entitled to participate in its deliberations.'

It was by virtue of this resolution that the respondents refused to permit the petitioner to vote.

A Constitutional Violation

Texas is free to conduct her elections and limit her electorate as she may deem wise, save only as her action may be affected by the prohibitions of the United States Constitution or in conflict with powers delegated to and exercised by the National Government. The Fourteenth Amendment forbids a state from making or enforcing any law which abridges the privileges or immunities of citizens of the United States and the Fifteenth Amendment specifically interdicts any denial or abridgement by a state of the right of citizens to vote on account of color. Respondents appeared in the District Court and the Circuit Court of Appeals and defended on the ground that the Democratic party of Texas is a voluntary organization with members banded together for the purpose of selecting individuals of the group representing the common political beliefs as candidates in the general election. As such a voluntary organization, it was claimed, the Democratic party is free to select its own membership and limit to whites participation in the party primary. Such action, the answer asserted, does not violate the Fourteenth, Fifteenth or Seventeenth Amendment as officers of government cannot be chosen at primaries and the Amendments are applicable only to general elections where governmental officers are actually elected. Primaries, it is said, are political party affairs, handled by party not governmental officers. No appearance for respondents is made in this Court. Arguments presented here by the Attorney General of Texas and the Chairman of the State Democratic Executive Committee of Texas, as amici curiae [friends of the court] urged substantially the same grounds as those advanced by the respondents.

The right of a Negro to vote in the Texas primary has been considered heretofore by this Court. The first case was *Nixon v. Herndon* [1927]. At that time, 1924, a Texas statute, declared 'in no event shall a Negro be eligible to participate in a Democratic party primary election . . . in the State of Texas.' Nixon was refused the right to vote in a Democratic primary and brought a suit for damages against the election officers. It was urged to this Court that the denial of the franchise that Nixon violated his Constitutional rights under the Fourteenth and Fifteenth Amendments. Without consideration of the Fifteenth, this Court held that the action of Texas in denying the ballot to Negroes by statute was in violation of the equal protection clause of the Fourteenth Amendment and reversed the dismissal of the suit.

The legislature of Texas reenacted the article but gave the State Executive Committee of a party the power to prescribe the qualifications of its members for voting or other participation. This article remains in the statutes. The State Executive Committee of the Democratic party adopted a resolution that white Democrats and none other might participate in the primaries of that party. Nixon was refused again the privilege of voting in a primary and again brought suit for damages. This Court again reversed the dismissal of the suit for the reason that the Committee action was deemed to be State action and invalid as discriminatory under the Fourteenth Amendment. The test was said to be whether the Committee operated as representative of the State in the discharge of the State's authority. The question of the inherent power of a political party in Texas 'without restraint by any law to determine its own membership' was open.

In *Grovey v. Townsend* [1935], this Court had before it another suit for damages for the refusal in a primary of a county clerk, a Texas officer with only public functions to perform, to furnish petitioner, a Negro, an absentee ballot. The refusal was solely on the ground of race. This case differed from *Nixon v. Condon* [1932], in that a state convention of the Democratic party had passed the resolution of May 24, 1932, hereinbefore quoted. It was decided that the determination by the state convention of the membership of the Democratic party made a significant change from a determination by the Executive Committee. The former was party action, voluntary in character. The latter, as had been held in the Condon case, was action by authority of the State. The managers of the primary election were therefore declared not to be state officials in such sense that their action was state action. A state convention of a party was said not to be an organ of the state. This Court went on to announce that to deny a vote in a primary was a mere refusal of party membership with which 'the state need have no concern,' while for a state to deny a vote in a general election on the ground of race or color violated the Constitution. Consequently, there was found no ground for holding that the county clerk's refusal of a ballot because of racial ineligibility for party membership denied the petitioner any right under the Fourteenth or Fifteenth Amendments.

Using Earlier Decisions

Since *Grovey v. Townsend* and prior to the present suit, no case from Texas involving primary elections has been before this Court. We did decide, however, *United States v. Classic* [1941]. We there held that Section 4 of Article I of the Constitution authorized Congress to regulate primary as well as general elections, 'where the primary is by law made an integral part of the election machinery.' Consequently, in the *Classic* case, we upheld the applicability to frauds in a Louisiana primary of 19 and 20 of the Criminal Code. Thereby corrupt acts of election officers were subjected to Congressional sanctions because that body had power to protect rights of Federal suffrage secured by the Constitution in primary as in general elections. This decision depended, too, on the determination that under the Louisiana statutes the primary was a part of the procedure for choice of Federal officials. By this decision the doubt as to whether or not such primaries were a part of 'elections' subject to Federal control, which had remained unanswered since *Newberry v. United States,* was erased. The *Nixon* cases were decided under the equal protection clause of the Fourteenth Amendment without a determination of the status of the primary as a part of the electoral process. The exclusion of Negroes from the primaries by action of the State was held invalid under that Amendment. The fusing by the *Classic* case of the primary and general elections into a single instrumentality for choice of officers has a definite bearing on the permissibility under the Constitution of excluding Negroes from primaries. This is not to say that the *Classic* case cuts directly into the rationale of *Grovey v. Townsend.* This latter case was not mentioned in the opinion. *Classic* bears upon *Grovey v. Townsend* not because exclusion of Negroes from primaries is any more or less state action by reason of the unitary character of the electoral process but because the recognition of the place of the primary in the electoral scheme makes clear that state delegation to a party of the power to fix the qualifications of primary elections is delegation of a state function that may make the party's action the action of the state. When *Grovey v. Townsend* was written, the Court looked upon the denial of a vote in a primary as a mere refusal by a party of party membership. As the Louisiana statutes for holding primaries are similar to those of Texas, our ruling in *Classic* as to the unitary character of the electoral process calls for a reexamination as to whether or not the exclusion of Negroes from a Texas party primary was state action.

The statutes of Texas relating to primaries and the resolution of the Democratic party of Texas extending the privileges of membership to white citizens only are the same in substance and effect today as they were when *Grovey v. Townsend* was decided by a unanimous Court. The question as to whether the exclusionary action of the party was the action of the State persists as the determinative factor. In again entering upon consideration of the inference to be drawn as to state action from a substantially similar factual situation, it should be noted that *Grovey v. Townsend* upheld exclusion of Negroes from primaries through the denial of party membership by a party convention. A few years before this Court refused approval of exclusion by the State Executive Committee of the party. A different result was reached on the theory that the Committee action was state authorized and the Convention action was unfettered by statutory control. Such a variation in the result from so slight a change in form influences us to consider anew the legal validity of the distinction which has resulted in barring Negroes from participating in the nominations of candidates of the Democratic party in Texas. Other precedents of this Court forbid the abridgement of the right to vote.

It may now be taken as a postulate that the right to vote in such a primary for the nomination of candidates without discrimination by the State, like the right to vote in a general election, is a right secured by the Constitution. By the terms of the Fifteenth Amendment that right may not be abridged by any state on account of race. Under our Constitution the great privilege of the ballot may not be denied a man by the State because of his color.

Congress Has the Right to Enforce the Fifteenth Amendment

Earl Warren

Attempts by many states to circumvent the Fifteenth Amendment by placing local restrictions on voting continued even after 1944's Smith v. Allwright decision. In 1965 Congress made a decisive attempt to outlaw these restrictions through a broad-based Voting Rights Act, which has since been renewed several times. Targeting most specifically the literacy tests that some Southern states used to stop African Americans from voting, the 1965 act proclaimed that states could no longer use such tests or other measures. In addition, it gave Congress regulatory power to ensure that any restrictions were indeed lifted.

The state of South Carolina complained that some provisions of the Voting Rights Act violated states' rights, since they required that a few states look to the federal government, in the person of then-attorney general Nicholas Katzenbach, in seeking approval for certain procedural changes. In January 1966 the Supreme Court rejected South Carolina's complaint and asserted that Congress's new powers were consistent with the Fifteenth Amendment's guarantees.

Earl Warren served as chief justice of the United States from 1953 to 1969 and presided over many landmark cases in U.S. history.

By leave of the Court, South Carolina has filed a bill of complaint, seeking a declaration that selected provisions of the Voting Rights Act of 1965 violate the Federal Constitution, and asking for an injunction against enforcement of

Earl Warren, "*South Carolina v. Katzenbach*, 383 U.S. 301 (1966)," U.S. Supreme Court, March 7, 1966. Reproduced by permission.

these provisions by the Attorney General. Original jurisdiction is founded on the presence of a controversy between a State and a citizen of another State under Art. III, 2, of the Constitution. Because no issues of fact were raised in the complaint, and because of South Carolina's desire to obtain a ruling prior to its primary elections in June 1966, we dispensed with appointment of a special master and expedited our hearing of the case.

Recognizing that the questions presented were of urgent concern to the entire country, we invited all of the States to participate in this proceeding as friends of the Court. A majority responded by submitting or joining in briefs on the merits, some supporting South Carolina and others the Attorney General. Seven of these States also requested and received permission to argue the case orally at our hearing. Without exception despite the emotional overtones of the proceeding, the briefs and oral arguments were temperate, lawyerlike and constructive. All viewpoints on the issues have been fully developed, and this additional assistance has been most helpful to the Court.

The Voting Rights Act was designed by Congress to banish the blight of racial discrimination in voting, which has infected the electoral process in parts of our country for nearly a century. The Act creates stringent new remedies for voting discrimination where it persists on a pervasive scale, and in addition, the statute strengthens existing remedies for pockets of voting discrimination elsewhere in the country. Congress assumed the power to prescribe these remedies from [section] 2 of the Fifteenth Amendment, which authorizes the National Legislature to effectuate by "appropriate" measures the constitutional prohibition against racial discrimination in voting. We hold that the sections of the Act which are properly before us are an appropriate means for carrying out Congress' constitutional responsibilities and are consonant with all other provisions of the Constitution. We therefore deny South Carolina's request that enforcement of these sections of the Act be enjoined.

A History of Discrimination

The constitutional propriety of the Voting Rights Act of 1965 must be judged with reference to the historical experience which it reflects. Before enacting the measure, Congress explored with great care the problem of racial discrimination in voting. The House and Senate Committees on the Judiciary each held hearings for nine days and received testimony from a total of 67 witnesses. More than three full days were consumed discussing the bill on the floor of the House, while the debate in the Senate covered 26 days in all. At the close of these deliberations, the verdict of both chambers was overwhelming. The House approved the bill by a vote of 328–74, and the measure passed the Senate by a margin of 79–18.

Two points emerge vividly from the voluminous legislative history of the Act contained in the committee hearings and floor debates. First: Congress felt itself confronted by an insidious and pervasive evil which had been perpetuated in certain parts of our country through unremitting and ingenious defiance of the Constitution. Second: Congress concluded that the unsuccessful remedies which it had prescribed in the past would have to be replaced by sterner and more elaborate measures in order to satisfy the clear commands of the Fifteenth Amendment. We pause here to summarize the majority reports of the House and Senate Committees, which document in considerable detail the factual basis for these reactions by Congress.

The Fifteenth Amendment to the Constitution was ratified in 1870. Promptly thereafter Congress passed the Enforcement Act of 1870, which made it a crime for public officers and private persons to obstruct exercise of the right to vote. The statute was amended in the following year to provide for detailed

John Doar, Nicholas Katzenbach, and Thurgood Marshall outside the U.S. Supreme Court in 1966. UPI/Corbis-Bettmann. Reproduced by permission.

federal supervision of the electoral process, from registration to the certification of returns. As the years passed and fervor for racial equality waned, enforcement of the laws became spotty and ineffective, and most of their provisions were repealed in 1894. The remnants have had little significance in the recently renewed battle against voting discrimination.

Tests for Voters

Meanwhile, beginning in 1890, the States of Alabama, Georgia, Louisiana, Mississippi, North Carolina, South Carolina, and Virginia enacted tests still in use which were specifically designed to prevent Negroes from voting. Typically, they made the ability to read and write a registration qualification and also required completion of a registration form. These laws were based on the fact that as of 1890 in each of the named States, more than two-thirds of the adult Negroes were illiterate while less than one-quarter of the adult whites were unable to read or write. At the same time, alternate tests were prescribed in all of the named States to assure that white illiterates would not be deprived of the franchise. These included grandfather clauses, property qualifications, "good character" tests, and the requirement that registrants "understand" or "interpret" certain matter.

The course of subsequent Fifteenth Amendment litigation in this Court demonstrates the variety and persistence of these and similar institutions designed to deprive Negroes of the right to vote. Grandfather clauses were invalidated in *Guinn v. United States* [1914], and *Myers v. Anderson* [1915]. Procedural hurdles were struck down in *Lane v. Wilson* [1939]. The white primary was outlawed in *Smith v. Allwright* [1944], and *Terry v. Adams* [1953]. Improper challenges were nullified in *United States v. Thomas* [1953]. Racial gerrymandering [the redrawing of voting districts] was forbidden by *Gomillion v. Lightfoot* [1960]. Finally, discriminatory application of voting tests was condemned in *Schnell v. Davis* [1949]; *Alabama v. United States* [1962], and *Louisiana v. United States* [1965].

According to the evidence in recent Justice Department voting suits, the latter stratagem is now the principal method used to bar Negroes from the polls. Discriminatory administration of voting qualifications has been found in all eight Alabama cases, in all nine Louisiana cases, and in all nine Mississippi cases which have gone to final judgment. Moreover, in almost all of these cases, the courts have held that the discrimination was pursuant to a widespread "pattern or practice." White applicants for registration have often been excused altogether from the literacy and understanding tests, or have been given easy versions, have received extensive help from voting officials, and have been registered despite serious errors in their answers. Negroes, on the other hand, have typically been required to pass difficult versions of all the tests without any outside assistance and without the slightest error. The good-morals requirement is so vague and subjective that it has constituted an open invitation to abuse at the hands of voting officials. Negroes obliged to obtain vouchers from registered voters have found it virtually impossible to comply in areas where almost no Negroes are on the rolls.

In recent years, Congress has repeatedly tried to cope with the problem by facilitating case-by-case litigation against voting discrimination. The Civil Rights Act of 1957 authorized the Attorney General to seek injunctions against public and private interference with the right to vote on racial grounds. Perfecting amendments in the Civil Rights Act of 1960 permitted the joinder of States as parties defendant, gave the Attorney General access to local voting records, and authorized courts to register voters in areas of systematic discrimination. Title I of the Civil Rights Act of 1964 expedited the hearing of voting cases before three-judge courts and outlawed some of the tactics used to disqualify Negroes from voting in federal elections.

Despite the earnest efforts of the Justice Department and of many federal judges, these new laws have done little to cure the problem of voting discrimination. According to estimates by the Attorney General during hearings on the Act, registration of voting-age Negroes in Alabama rose only from 14.2% to 19.4% between 1958 and 1964; in Louisiana it barely inched ahead from 31.7% to 31.8% between 1956 and 1965; and in Mississippi it increased only from 4.4% to 6.4% between 1954 and 1964. In each instance, registration of voting-age whites ran roughly 50 percentage points or more ahead of Negro registration. . . .

National vs. States' Rights

Provisions of the Voting Rights Act of 1965 are challenged on the fundamental ground that they exceed the powers of Congress and encroach on an area reserved to the States by the Constitution. South Carolina and certain of the *amici curiae* [friends of the court] also attack specific sections of the Act for more particular reasons. They argue that the coverage formula prescribed in 4(a)–(d) violates the principle of the equality of States, denies due process by employing an invalid presumption and by barring judicial review of administrative findings, constitutes a forbidden bill of attainder, and impairs the separation of powers by adjudicating guilt through legislation. They claim that the review of new voting rules required in 5 infringes Article III by directing the District Court to issue advisory opinions. They contend that the assignment of federal examiners authorized in 6(b) abridges due process by precluding judicial review of administrative findings and impairs the separation of powers by giving the Attorney General judicial functions; also that the challenge procedure prescribed in 9 denies due process on account of its speed. Finally, South Carolina and certain of the amici curiae maintain that 4(a) and 5, buttressed by 14(b) of the Act, abridge due process by limiting litigation to a distant forum.

Some of these contentions may be dismissed at the outset. The word "person" in the context of the Due Process Clause of the Fifth Amendment cannot, by any reasonable mode of interpretation, be expanded to encompass the States of the Union, and to our knowledge this has never been done by any court. Likewise, courts have consistently regarded the Bill of Attainder Clause of Article I and the principle of the separation of powers only as protections for individual persons and private groups, those who are peculiarly vulnerable to nonjudicial determinations of guilt. Nor does a State have standing as the parent of its citizens to invoke these constitutional provisions against the Federal Government, the ultimate *parens patriae* [parent of the nation] of every American citizen. The objections to the Act which are raised under these provisions may therefore be considered only as additional aspects of the basic question presented by the case: Has Congress exercised its powers under the Fifteenth Amendment in an appropriate manner with relation to the States?

The ground rules for resolving this question are clear. The language and purpose of the Fifteenth Amendment, the prior decisions construing its several provisions, and the general doctrines of constitutional interpretation, all point to one fundamental principle. As against the reserved powers of the States, Congress may use any rational means to effectuate the constitutional prohibition of racial discrimination in voting. . . .

The basic test to be applied in a case involving 2 of the Fifteenth Amendment is the same as in all cases concerning the express powers of Congress with relation to the reserved powers of the States. Chief Justice [John] Marshall [served 1801–1835] laid down the classic formulation, 50 years before the Fifteenth Amendment was ratified:

> "Let the end be legitimate, let it be within the scope of the constitution, and all means which are appropriate, which are plainly adapted to that end, which are not prohibited, but consist with the letter and spirit of the constitution, are constitutional."

The Court has subsequently echoed his language in describing each of the Civil War Amendments:

> "Whatever legislation is appropriate, that is, adapted to carry out the objects the amendments have in view, whatever tends to enforce submission to the prohibitions they contain, and to secure to all persons the enjoyment of perfect equality of civil rights and the equal protection of the laws against State denial or invasion, if not prohibited, is brought within the domain of congressional power."

This language was again employed, nearly 50 years later, with reference to Congress' related authority under 2 of the Eighteenth Amendment.

We therefore reject South Carolina's argument that Congress may appropriately do no more than to forbid violations of the Fifteenth Amendment in general terms—that the task of fashioning specific remedies or of applying them to particular localities must necessarily be left entirely to the courts. Congress is not circumscribed by any such artificial rules under [section] 2 of the Fifteenth Amendment. In the oft-repeated words of Chief Justice Marshall, referring to another specific legislative authorization in the Constitution, "This power, like all others vested in Congress, is complete in itself, may be exercised to its utmost extent, and acknowledges no limitations, other than are prescribed in the constitution." . . .

The bill of complaint is dismissed.

Parts of the Voting Rights Act Are Unconstitutional

Hugo Black

Justice Black mostly agreed with the Supreme Court's majority opinion in South Carolina v. Katzenbach, *acknowledging that 1965's Voting Rights Act did indeed give Congress the right to ensure that individual states did not use literacy tests or other measures to deny the vote to members of minority groups. This, he claimed, was consistent with the Fifteenth Amendment's guarantees. But he argued that the Court went too far in concluding that states must convince federal officials that any changes to their voting laws or procedures did not violate the act. Such a requirement was, according to Black, an unconstitutional imposition of federal power over the rights and freedoms of the states.*

I agree with substantially all of the Court's opinion sustaining the power of Congress under [section] 2 of the Fifteenth Amendment to suspend state literacy tests and similar voting qualifications and to authorize the Attorney General to secure the appointment of federal examiners to register qualified voters in various sections of the country. Section 1 of the Fifteenth Amendment provides that "The right of citizens of the United States to vote shall not be denied or abridged by the United States or by any State on account of race, color, or previous condition of servitude." In addition to this unequivocal command to the States and the Federal Government that no citizen shall have his right to vote denied or abridged because of race or color, [section] 2 of the Amendment unmistakably gives Congress specific power to go further and pass appropriate legislation to protect this right to vote against any method of abridgment no matter how subtle. . . . I have no

Hugo Black, "*South Carolina v. Katzenbach*, 383 U.S. 301 (1966)," U.S. Supreme Court, March 7, 1966. Reproduced by permission.

doubt whatever as to the power of Congress under 2 to enact the provisions of the Voting Rights Act of 1965 dealing with the suspension of state voting tests that have been used as notorious means to deny and abridge voting rights on racial grounds. This same congressional power necessarily exists to authorize appointment of federal examiners. I also agree with the judgment of the Court upholding 4(b) of the Act, which sets out a formula for determining when and where the major remedial sections of the Act take effect. I reach this conclusion, however, for a somewhat different reason than that stated by the Court, which is that "the coverage formula is rational in both practice and theory." I do not base my conclusion on the fact that the formula is rational, for it is enough for me that Congress by creating this formula has merely exercised its hitherto unquestioned and undisputed power to decide when, where, and upon what conditions its laws shall go into effect. By stating in specific detail that the major remedial sections of the Act are to be applied in areas where certain conditions exist, and by granting the Attorney General and the Director of the Census unreviewable power to make the mechanical determination of which areas come within the formula of 4(b), I believe that Congress has acted within its established power to set out preconditions upon which the Act is to go into effect.

An Area of Dissent

Though, as I have said, I agree with most of the Court's conclusions, I dissent from its holding that every part of [section] 5 of the Act is constitutional. Section 4(a), to which 5 is linked, suspends for five years all literacy tests and similar devices in those States coming within the formula of 4(b). Section 5 goes on to provide that a State covered by 4(b) can in no way amend its constitution or laws relating to voting without first trying to persuade the Attorney General of the United States or the Federal District Court for the District of Columbia that the new proposed laws do not have the purpose and will not have the effect of denying the right to vote to citizens on account of their race or color. I think this section is unconstitutional on at least two grounds.

(a) The Constitution gives federal courts jurisdiction over cases and controversies only. If it can be said that any case or controversy arises under this section which gives the District Court for the District of Columbia jurisdiction to approve or reject state laws or constitutional amendments, then the case or controversy must be between a State and the United States Government. But it is hard for me to believe that a justiciable controversy can arise in the constitutional sense from a desire by the United States Government or some of its officials to determine in advance what legislative provisions a State may enact or what constitutional amendments it may adopt. If this dispute between the Federal Government and the States amounts to a case or controversy it is a far cry from the traditional constitutional notion of a case or controversy as a dispute over the meaning of enforceable laws or the manner in which they are applied. And if by this section Congress has created a case or controversy, and I do not believe it has, then it seems to me that the most appropriate judicial forum for settling these important questions is this Court acting under its original Art. III, 2, jurisdiction to try cases in which a State is a party. At least a trial in this Court would treat the States with the dignity to which they should be entitled as constituent members of our Federal Union.

The form of words and the manipulation of presumptions used in 5 to create the illusion of a case or controversy should not be allowed to cloud the effect of that section. By requiring a State to ask a federal court to approve the validity of a proposed law which has in no way become operative, Congress has asked the State to secure precisely the type of advisory opinion our Constitution forbids. As I have pointed out elsewhere, . . . some of those drafting our Constitution wanted to give the federal courts the power to issue advisory opinions and propose new laws to the legislative body. These suggestions were rejected. We should likewise reject any attempt by Congress to flout constitutional limitations by authorizing federal courts to render advisory opinions when there is no case or controversy before them. Congress has ample power to protect the rights of citizens to vote without resorting to the unnecessarily circuitous, indirect and unconstitutional route it has adopted in this section.

Excessive Federal Power

(b) My second and more basic objection to 5 is that Congress has here exercised its power under 2 of the Fifteenth Amendment through the adoption of means that conflict with the most basic principles of the Constitution. As the Court says the limitations of the power granted under 2 are the same as the limitations imposed on the exercise of any of the powers expressly granted Congress by the Constitution. The classic formulation of these constitutional limitations was stated by Chief Justice [John] Marshall when he said in *McCulloch v. Maryland* [1819], "Let the end be legitimate, let it be within the scope of the constitution, and all means which are appropriate, which are plainly adapted to that end, which are not prohibited, but consist with the letter and spirit of the constitution, are constitutional." Section 5, by providing that some of the States cannot pass state laws or adopt state constitutional amendments without first being compelled to beg federal authorities to approve their policies, so distorts our constitutional structure of government as to render any distinction drawn in the Constitution between state and federal power almost meaningless. One of the most basic premises upon which our structure of government was founded was that the Federal Government was to have certain specific and limited powers and no others, and all other power was to be reserved either "to the States respectively, or to the people." Certainly if all the provisions of our Constitution which limit the power of the Federal Government and reserve other power to the States are to mean anything, they mean at least that the States have power to pass laws and amend their constitutions without first sending their officials hundreds of miles away to beg federal authorities to approve them. Moreover, it seems to me that 5 which gives federal officials power to veto state laws they do not like is in direct conflict with the clear command of our Constitution that "The United States shall guarantee to every State in this Union a Republican Form of Government." I cannot help but believe that the inevitable effect of any such law which forces any one of the States to entreat federal authorities in far-away places for approval of local laws before they can become effective is to create the impression that the State or States treated in this way are little more than conquered provinces. And if one law concerning voting can make the States plead for this approval by a distant federal court or the United States Attorney General, other laws on different subjects can force the States to seek the advance approval not only of the Attorney General but of the President himself or any other chosen members of his staff. It is inconceivable to me that such a radical degradation of state power was intended in any of the provisions of our Constitution or its Amendments. Of course I do not mean to cast any doubt whatever upon the indisputable power of the Federal Government to invalidate a state law once enacted and operative on the ground that it intrudes into the area of supreme federal power. But the Federal Government has heretofore always been content to exercise this power to protect federal supremacy by authorizing its agents to bring lawsuits against state officials once an operative state law has created an actual case and controversy. A federal law which assumes the power to compel the States to submit in advance any proposed legislation they have for approval by federal agents approaches dangerously near to wiping the States out as useful and effective units in the government of our country. I cannot agree to any constitutional interpretation that leads inevitably to such a result.

No Right to Veto State Laws

I see no reason to read into the Constitution meanings it did not have when it was adopted and which have not been put into it since. The proceedings of the original Constitutional Convention show beyond all doubt that the power to veto or negative state laws was denied Congress. On several occasions proposals were submitted to the convention to grant this power to Congress. These proposals were debated extensively and on every occasion when submitted for vote they were overwhelmingly rejected. The refusal to give Congress this extraordinary power to veto state laws was based on the belief that if such power resided in Congress the States would be helpless to function as effective governments. Since that time neither the Fifteenth Amendment nor any other Amendment to the Constitution has given the slightest indication of a purpose to grant Congress the power to veto state laws either by itself or its agents, Nor does any provision in the Constitution endow the federal courts with power to participate with state legislative bodies in determining what state policies shall be enacted into law. The judicial power to invalidate a law in a case or controversy after the law has become effective is a long way from the power to prevent a State from passing a law. I cannot agree with the Court that Congress—denied a power in itself to veto a state law—can delegate this same power to the Attorney General or the District Court for the District of Columbia. For the effect on the States is the same in both cases—they cannot pass their laws without sending their agents to the City of Washington to plead to federal officials for their advance approval.

In this and other prior Acts Congress has quite properly vested the Attorney General with extremely broad power to protect voting rights of citizens against discrimination on account of race or color. Section 5 viewed in this context is of very minor importance and in my judgment is likely to serve more as an irritant to the States than as an aid to the enforcement of the Act. I would hold 5 invalid for the reasons stated above with full confidence that the Attorney General has ample power to give vigorous, expeditious and effective protection to the voting rights of all citizens.

Ensuring Voting Rights in Contemporary America

Indiana's Voter ID Law Threatens to Disenfranchise Some Voters

Cynthia Tucker

In April 2008, the Supreme Court of the United States upheld a decision made in the state of Indiana to require voters to present some form of government-approved photo identification, such as a driver's license or passport, before they could cast their ballots. The intent of Indiana officials was to discourage voter fraud, and the majority of the Supreme Court agreed that requiring photo identification was a legitimate and reasonable requirement for voters.

In the following selection, journalist Cynthia Tucker takes issue with the decision. She claims that it is unreasonable to expect certain groups of people to keep government-issued photo identification, since not all people need or use them in their daily lives or are capable of acquiring them. Furthermore, she notes, not all voters were even aware of the requirement. She suspects that the motivation for the requirement was to disenfranchise voters who are likely to cast their ballots for Democratic Party candidates.

Cynthia Tucker is an editorial page editor and columnist for the Atlanta Journal Constitution.

Congratulations to the Indiana Legislature, whose harsh voter ID law has ferreted out a suspicious bunch who tried to cast ballots without proper identification in the [2008] Democratic primary. Who do those old ladies think they are, American citizens?

Cynthia Tucker, "Voter ID Law Religious in its Absurdity," *Atlanta Journal Constitution*, May 11, 2008. Copyright © 2008 The Atlanta Journal-Constitution. Republished with permission of The Atlanta Journal/Constitution conveyed through Copyright Clearance Center, Inc.

Actually, that's exactly what they are. Several retired nuns who have been voting all their lives were prohibited from casting ballots in South Bend because they didn't have proper ID. The nuns, who live at a convent, went to their polling place on the ground floor. There was absolutely no doubt about their identity, since the poll workers included other nuns from St. Mary's Convent, near the University of Notre Dame.

A couple of sisters showed expired passports, but the law doesn't allow those, either. (If you were born in the U.S.A., that doesn't change, no matter how outdated your passport.) Indiana's law is so restrictive that even out-of-state driver's licenses are not accepted, a significant problem for college students who register to vote while attending Notre Dame, Indiana University or other colleges.

If the absurdity of punitive voter ID laws—adopted in several states with GOP-dominated legislatures, including Georgia—was not apparent before now, this case ought to help all but the most partisan see the fallacy. Two weeks ago [late April 2008], in a ruling that spurns the universal franchise, the Supreme Court upheld Indiana's ID requirements. Writing for the 6–3 majority, Justice John Paul Stevens asserted that there was no "concrete evidence of the burden imposed on voters who now lack photo identification."

How about the vicious proposition of throwing out the ballots of elderly nuns, law-abiding citizens who have given their lives to the purest form of volunteer service? How about the burden of forcing them to go get a state-sponsored photo ID?

Indiana Secretary of State Todd Rokita was even more contemptuous of disenfranchised voters, telling reporters that "the sisters were aware of the photo ID requirements and chose not to follow them." Nonsense, says John Borkowski, a South Bend attorney and volunteer election watchdog with the Lawyers' Committee for Civil Rights Under Law.

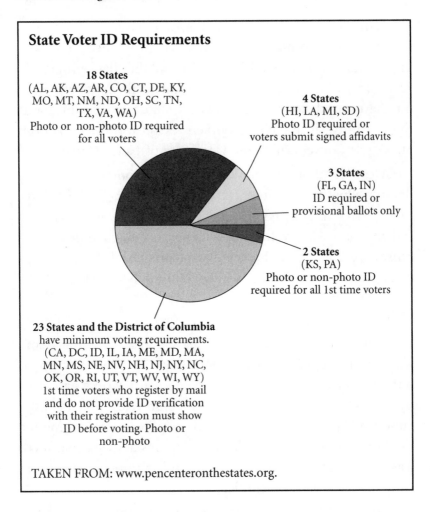

State Voter ID Requirements

18 States
(AL, AK, AZ, AR, CO, CT, DE, KY, MO, MT, NM, ND, OH, SC, TN, TX, VA, WA)
Photo or non-photo ID required for all voters

4 States
(HI, LA, MI, SD)
Photo ID required or voters submit signed affidavits

3 States
(FL, GA, IN)
ID required or provisional ballots only

2 States
(KS, PA)
Photo or non-photo ID required for all 1st time voters

23 States and the District of Columbia
have minimum voting requirements.
(CA, DC, ID, IL, IA, ME, MD, MA, MN, MS, NE, NV, NH, NJ, NY, NC, OK, OR, RI, UT, VT, WV, WI, WY)
1st time voters who register by mail and do not provide ID verification with their registration must show ID before voting. Photo or non-photo

TAKEN FROM: www.pencenteronthestates.org.

Borkowski says some of the nuns—described as mostly in their 80s and 90s and no longer driving—were not aware of the law. A couple of others had tried to get to a motor vehicle office to get an official photo ID but were unable to do so. "I don't think it's fair to say these are people who chose not to comply with the law," Borkowski said.

Voter Fraud Not the Real Issue

Supporters of harsh voter ID laws claim that state-sponsored photo identification is necessary to prevent in-person fraud at the ballot box. But that sort of illegal voting simply doesn't exist. It's urban legend, like stories of homeless people kidnapped for their kidneys.

Yes, yes, I know that voter fraud exists. But the vast majority occurs through absentee ballots, which don't have to be cast in person. If ferreting out fraud were the point of restrictive voter ID laws, state legislatures would tighten up on the requirements for absentee ballots. There has been precious little of that.

Instead, those who tout the fraud-preventing brilliance of voter ID laws note that those without official IDs can use absentee ballots if they feel so strongly about the franchise. Rokita offered absentee ballots as Indiana's "safety net" for those without state-sanctioned ID.

So what's the real motive for these punitive voter ID laws? Republicans are trying to block the ballots of a few poor and elderly voters, those least likely to have driver's licenses. It's probably no coincidence that those blocs tend to support Democrats. (Indiana's prohibition against out-of-state licenses would also work against all those Obama-loving college students.)

President [George W.] Bush has touted democracy in Afghanistan and Iraq, proudly pointing to the purple-ink-stained fingers of voters who were able to cast ballots without fear of political retribution. But in this country, the president's political party denies the ballot to elderly nuns.

Voter ID Laws Have Not Been Shown to Reduce Voter Turnout

Jeff Milyo

In the following selection, Jeff Milyo claims that Indiana's law requiring voters to present photo identification is a reasonable way to both discourage voter fraud and make the voting process more efficient. He cites studies suggesting that such laws do not have much effect on total voter turnout, since most of those who vote in the first place are likely to have no problem presenting the proper identification. Most of those who do not have it, he asserts, are unlikely to vote anyway. Because of these factors voter ID laws do not amount to attempts to deny Fifteenth Amendment rights to poor, minority, or elderly voters.

Jeff Milyo is professor of economics at the University of Missouri and a senior fellow at the Cato Institute.

Every state requires voters to produce some evidence they are eligible to vote, but Indiana's photo identification requirements are the most stringent. The Supreme Court will soon decide whether the state can require official photo ID to cast a regular ballot at the polls. If the law is upheld, several other states are likely to follow Indiana's example.

Opinion polls suggest most people find voter ID laws to be reasonable precautions against ballot stuffing; however, many progressive activists consider these reforms undemocratic and discriminatory. They argue such laws are unnecessary because voter impersonation at the polls is a myth, and they worry identification requirements unduly burden eligible voters, especially minorities, the elderly, poor and less educated.

Georgia governor Sonny Perdue is backed by Senator Cecil Stanton, sponsor of the Voter ID legislation in the Senate, as he holds up a sample photo Voter ID, after signing the bill into law in Atlanta in 2006. AP Images.

Armed with this intuition, opponents of the photo ID law have made dire predictions about declining voter turnout, particularly among disadvantaged groups. Such claims are easily tested, but the public debate has nevertheless been mostly unencumbered by facts.

Voters Deterred for Other Reasons

First, decades of social science research indicate voter identification requirements should have at most negligible effects on turnout. This is because there are already many hurdles to casting a ballot, from taking an interest in public affairs to registering to vote and bothering to remember where and when to vote. Almost all nonvoting is explained by these mundane factors.

For example, the 2006 Current Population Survey from the U.S. Census Bureau contains information on the voting behavior of about 85,000 people; among eligible voters who did not vote, 94 percent were either not registered to vote, forgot to vote or weren't interested in voting, etc. So the few folks who don't have official photo identification are already unlikely to be voters for any number of reasons unrelated to voter identification requirements at the polls.

But those eligible voters with the wherewithal to register, study the candidates, remember where and when to vote and get themselves to the polls are unlikely to be deterred by the added requirement of photo identification. Fewer still are incapable of producing identification if so motivated.

Second, while most of the remaining nonvoters give undescribed "other" reasons for not voting, just less than 2 percent of eligible nonvoters do cite registration problems as their primary reason for not voting. This figure includes people who are not properly registered and perhaps some who merely lack proof. These nonvoters, however, are not disproportionately located in Indiana, despite that state's more restrictive ID requirements. Nor is it the case that minority, less educated, elderly or poor Indiana citizens are more likely to be nonvoters because of registration problems. Therefore, self-reported voting behavior should allay most concerns about photo ID.

Third, actual election returns further demonstrate Indiana's law did not have a negative impact on voter turnout. The 2002 and 2006 midterm elections straddle the implementation of the photo ID requirements in Indiana and so offer a natural experiment to test effects on turnout. I have examined county-level election returns from Indiana before and after photo ID, and voter turnout actually increased about 2 percent. Nor was turnout relatively lower in counties with greater percentages of minority, less educated, elderly or poor voters. These findings are robust to a variety of statistical assumptions and hold up when more years are included in the analysis.

The final reason voter turnout is unlikely to change much in the wake of photo ID is that voter impersonation is itself probably rare. Despite popular concerns that too many ineligible votes are cast in elections, many progressives ridicule the idea of voter fraud at the polls. The choice of words is key;

"fraud" requires intent and is understandably difficult to prove. But do voter identification laws prevent ineligible votes from canceling out legal votes?

Safeguarding Proper Ballots

An indication comes from the 2000 Current Population Survey. Respondents were asked whether they had moved in the past five years and whether they had registered to vote in the past five years. More than 10 percent of respondents—both nationally and in Indiana—self-reported they were not registered at their current residence but voted anyway. Of course, some of these responses might be in error, but the implication is a non-trivial number of improper ballots are cast in a typical election. So even absent irrefutable proof of vote fraud, there is still good reason to check voter ID at the polls.

Photo ID prevents ineligible voters from entering the voting booth and induces otherwise eligible voters to update their registration ahead of time. Reasonable people might weigh the benefits and costs differently, but one thing is certain: Far from being a nefarious contrivance to disenfranchise vulnerable citizens, Indiana's photo ID law is nothing more than a common-sense means to administer elections more effectively and fairly for all citizens.

States Continue to Find Ways to Restrict Voters

Adam Cohen

Despite the Fifteenth Amendment's guarantees, a series of Su-
preme Court decisions, and the voting rights acts of 1965 and
1993, the struggle to ensure voting privileges for all continues, as
Adam Cohen indicates in the following selection. One important
issue is that voting procedures continue to be under the control
of individual states, and state laws and practices vary widely. As
Cohen notes, one result of this was the fiasco in the presidential
election of the year 2000, when the state of Florida failed to
reach a result due to numerous voting problems, which ulti-
mately brought about Supreme Court involvement.

Suspecting that these measures have the effect of disenfran-
chising voters, Cohen argues that the federal government, through
Congress, should establish uniform voting practices across the
states. He claims that it has this right based on the Constitution
and that such measures would make irrelevant such controver-
sies as that in Florida in 2000 and Indiana's 2008 decision to re-
quire voters to present photo identification.

Adam Cohen is an assistant editorial page editor at The
New York Times.

It would be hard for Florida to surpass its disastrous performance in the 2000 election, but give the Sunshine State
credit for trying. Its latest assault on democracy: a law threat-
ening volunteer groups with crippling fines if they make small
mistakes in registering voters. The law seems clearly aimed at
keeping new voters—especially minorities and the poor—off
the rolls. And it is working. The League of Women Voters,
which has registered Florida voters since 1939, has called off
its registration drive this year [2008].

Florida is not the only state trying to stop eligible people from voting. Georgia passed a law in 2005 that made voters pay for their voter ID cards—a modern poll tax. The fee was eventually removed, but the law could still block as many as 300,000 registered voters without the right ID from casting ballots. In 2004, Ohio ordered counties to throw out voter registration forms that were not on thick enough paper.

Voting Restrictions Should Be Old News

It is chilling to think that state legislators and election officials would intentionally try to make it harder for Americans to vote, but they always have—with poll taxes, literacy tests and gerrymandering [redrawing voting districts]. There was a time when the Supreme Court regularly struck these restrictions down. In 1966, it held Virginia's $1.50 poll tax unconstitutional. In 1972, it ruled that Tennessee's one-year residency requirement for voting violated the Constitution.

Now the Supreme Court has switched sides. This week [late April 2008], it upheld a harsh Indiana voter ID law that could disenfranchise many poor, elderly and student voters. The ruling will make it even easier for other states to block voters' access to the ballot box.

Congress Should Uphold Voting Rights

If the courts won't protect voters, Congress has to. The Constitution, in Article 1, Section 4, gives Congress broad authority to set the rules for federal elections. It should use this power to set minimum voting rights standards that would apply nationwide and ensure that all eligible Americans could vote.

Voter registration rules are the place to start. Federal law should hold organizations like the League of Women Voters harmless if they make good-faith mistakes while registering people. There should be a federal voter registration form, usable in any state, and uniform regulations so Ohio could not throw out forms based on paper thickness and Florida could not bar voters, as it now does, from fixing small errors on a form within a month of an election.

Congress should also regulate voter challenges at the polls. Parties and candidates often use bad-faith challenges as a dirty trick—to intimidate voters or to slow down voting in certain neighborhoods. Senator Sheldon Whitehouse, Democrat of Rhode Island, has a good bill that would require challengers who are not election officials to sign an affidavit stating why they believe a specific voter is not eligible.

Ballot formats should be standardized nationally rather than left to the often bad judgment of local officials. [Florida's] Palm Beach County's butterfly ballot, which apparently changed the outcome of the 2000 presidential election, got a lot of attention, but there are confusing ballots in use across the country.

The patchwork of state ID laws should be replaced by a single standard that allows people to present any of an array of identification, including college IDs, and permits voters to sign an affidavit if they do not have ID.

There are many other problems that need to be fixed. Some states' rules for provisional ballots—used when election officials cannot find a voter's name on the rolls—are clearly designed to disqualify a large number of ballots from eligible voters.

Congress also needs to set a minimum standard for the number of voting machines per voter and ensure that states allocate them equitably. There were widespread reports in Ohio in 2004 of voters in poor, black neighborhoods waiting hours to vote while white neighborhoods had no lines. At Kenyon College, students waited up to 10 hours.

Good reform bills have been introduced in Congress, including ones backed by Senators Barack Obama and Hillary Rodham Clinton. But they have faced strong partisan opposition, and lobbying from influential state and local election officials. Critics of reform make the specious argument that states have the right to set the rules for federal elections. The founders, when they wrote the Constitution, said otherwise.

Some Authorities Still Try to Stop African Americans from Voting

Art Levine

According to journalist Art Levine, the author of the following selection, some officials in the contemporary Republican Party continue to try to deny the vote to African Americans nearly 140 years after the ratification of the Fifteenth Amendment. He uses the occasion of the April 4 anniversary of the assassination of civil rights leader Martin Luther King Jr. to make his point. King, killed in 1968, was instrumental in seeing that earlier challenges to the Fifteenth Amendment's guarantees were overturned.

Levine argues that Republican activists target mostly minority voters, since they are likely to support the Democratic Party. In doing so, they often use measures intended, ostensibly, to discourage voter fraud. Levine, citing other experts, suggests that voter fraud is an overstated threat and that the motives of those who challenge voter registration recall those of earlier opponents of the Fifteenth Amendment.

Art Levine is a contributing editor to Washington Monthly *magazine.*

While remembering the life and death of Dr. Martin Luther King, it's worth noting that Republican operatives and the [George W.] Bush administration's Department of Justice have turned back the clock on civil rights. They have created a new set of Jim Crow–like policies and strategies with a still-active goal: stopping blacks, who lean Democratic, from casting ballots that count.

Art Levine, "Forty Years After MLK's Death: DOJ's War on Black Voters," The Huffington Post, April 4, 2008. Copyright © 2008 HuffingtonPost.com. Reproduced by permission.

Have Justice Department officials and GOP loyalists become essentially an upscale, white-collar version of the [Ku Klux] Klan, armed with voting lists on their Palm Pilots rather than burning crosses and guns to keep blacks from voting?

Race Restrictions Still Exist

This week [first week of April], a series of articles have been published online underscoring the ways that the racist restrictions of the past have been revived, in often disturbing ways. In the *Huffington Post*, I reported how the FBI ignored threats to jail voters in Dallas during a hard-fought 2006 state legislative race. The Campaign Legal Center today demanded an in-depth Justice Department probe of its failure to investigate this blatant violation of civil rights.

The full story behind these sorts of vote-suppressing schemes is told in the latest issue of *The American Prospect*, which explores, in "The Republican War on Voting," how local, state and federal officials and GOP operatives targeted the community group ACORN [Association of Community Organizations for Reform Now] with phony claims of voter fraud because of its successful voter registration drives. The claims of widespread voter fraud live on in briefs supporting the Indiana photo ID law, filed by the federal government, the state and conservative Republicans, now before the Supreme Court.

What was once primarily a series of tactics stretching back from the evil days of the poll tax in the 1960s to "caging" [using the mail to challenge voter registration] and photo ID today, has become official Justice Department policy—either by ignoring threats to black voting rights or active steps to disenfranchise them and most other low-income minorities. [Elections expert] Steve Rosenfeld in *Social Policy* looks at the full scope of vote-suppression strategies pursued by the Justice Department, pulling together a complete picture of its lawsuits, rulings and advisory actions aimed at promoting photo

ID, ignoring threats to the civil rights of blacks and promoting massive purging of voter rolls.

As Project Vote noted in an overview of these articles:

> Three recent articles made available online this week—including two by Art Levine and one by Steve Rosenfeld—focus on the partisan subversion of the Department of Justice and show how partisan schemes to engage in widespread voter suppression targeted one of the most active defenders of the rights of poor people and people of color. These articles have exposed what amounts to an entire war waged by conservatives against the voting rights gains of the past generation. Taken in total, the picture that emerges shows nothing less than an attempt to take America back to days of segregation and Jim Crow except this time the marauders are wearing suits and ties and carry briefcases rather than wearing white hoods and sheets and burning crosses. Even more disturbing is their willingness to subvert the nonpartisan nature of the nation's top law enforcement institution, the Department of Justice and commit the resources of the Federal government to the systematic disenfranchisement of American citizens.

As my piece in the *American Prospect* points out:

> [Attacking ACORN has been part of] the Republican Party's ongoing nationwide campaign to suppress the low-income minority vote by propagating the myth of voter fraud. Using various tactics—including media smears, bogus lawsuits, restrictive new voting laws and policies, and flimsy prosecutions—Republican operatives, election officials, and the GOP-controlled Justice Department have limited voting access and gone after voter-registration groups such as ACORN. Which should come as no surprise: In building support for initiatives raising the minimum wage and kindred ballot measures, ACORN has registered, in partnership with Project Vote, 1.6 million largely Democratic-leaning voters since 2004. All told, non-profit groups registered over three million new voters in 2004, about the same time that

Protestors march during the Shadow Inauguration demonstration in Washington on January 20, 2001, following the presidential inauguration of George W. Bush. The demonstration was to protest disenfranchisement of African American voters and to defend the Voting Rights Act. AP Images.

Republican and Justice Department efforts to publicize voter fraud and limit voting access became more widespread. And attacking ACORN has been a central element of a systematic GOP disenfranchisement agenda to undermine Democratic prospects before each Election Day.

Revelations that U.S. attorneys were fired for their failure to successfully prosecute voter fraud have revealed how fictitious the allegations of widespread fraud actually were—but the allegations haven't gone away. They live on in all the vote-suppressing laws and regulations that will likely affect [2008's] election, in GOP rhetoric and, most recently, in the arguments presented by champions of Indiana's restrictive voter-identification law in a case currently before the U.S. Supreme Court.

Voter Fraud Is a Myth

Unfortunately, progressives have tended to pay more attention to Election Day dirty tricks and to electronic voting machines than to a more systemic threat: the Republican campaign to suppress the votes of low-income, young, and minority voters through restrictive legislation and rulings, all based on the mythic specter of voter fraud. Those relatively transient voters, drawn to the polls this year by the [Barack] Obama and [Hillary] Clinton campaigns, could find themselves thwarted in November and thereafter by the GOP-driven regime of voting restrictions—particularly if, as many observers believe, the Court upholds Indiana's restrictive law before it adjourns this June. [The Indiana law was upheld.]

> Voter fraud is actually less likely to occur than lightning striking a person, according to data compiled by New York University's Brennan Center for Justice. As Lorraine Minnite, a Columbia University professor, observed in the Project Vote report, The Politics of Voter Fraud, "The claim that voter fraud threatens the integrity of American elections is itself a fraud."

While we remember Dr. King, there's still long way to go to achieve the voting rights he fought so hard to achieve.

Federal Officials Still Monitor Elections to Ensure Fair Voting Procedures

Katherine Sayre

Journalist Katherine Sayre writes in the following selection that the fight to ensure fair voting at the local level is an ongoing one. She cites a news release from the United States Department of Justice that reports that officials will go to the small Alabama town of Bayou La Batre to make sure that all who have the right to vote can do so without harassment or intimidation in a local election held in August 2008.

While the Fifteenth Amendment was enacted to secure voting rights for African Americans, the controversy in Bayou La Batre concerns members of another minority group, Vietnamese Americans attracted to the region's fishing industry. Sayre writes that some members of this community have had their right to vote challenged based on citizenship or other alleged complaints.

Katherine Sayre is a journalist whose articles are syndicated in newspapers around the country.

U.S. Department of Justice officials will monitor the treatment of voters at the polls in [the August 26, 2008,] municipal election in Bayou La Batre [Alabama], according to a news release.

They will watch over the election to ensure compliance with the Voting Rights Act, a federal law that protects minority voting rights and bans discrimination at the polls, according to the release. . . .

Katherine Sayre, "Feds to Monitor Election in Bayou La Batre," *Press Register*, August 26, 2008. Reproduced by permission.

Protecting Asian-American Voters Rights

It's not the first time that federal officials have overseen elections in the seafood and shipbuilding town on the Alabama coast.

In 2004, Justice Department observers monitored an October runoff election amid concerns about discrimination against Asian-American voters who went to the polls in an August municipal election.

About one-third of the city's population of 2,300 is Asian-American, according to the 2000 U.S. Census.

Opponents of the first Vietnamese-American candidate for a city office, Phuong Tan Huynh, challenged the ballots of more than two dozen Asian voters at the polls.

The challengers, supporters of incumbent Jackie Ladnier, claimed the voters were either not U.S. citizens or city residents or had felony convictions that stripped them of voting rights.

Supporters of Huynh said the challenges were intended to intimidate Asian voters from casting their ballots.

Huynh went on to win a four-year term in the runoff. He did not file for re-election [in 2008].

Minh Le, a Vietnamese-American candidate for a council seat in today's election, said he hopes the Justice Department's monitoring will ensure that the election is "fair for everyone."

According to the Justice Department's news release, voters who want to file a complaint alleging discriminatory voting practices—including harassment or intimidation—can call the Civil Rights Division at 1-800-253-3931.

The Justice Department sends hundreds of federal observers to elections across the country each year, according to the release.

Appendices

Appendix A

The Amendments to the U.S. Constitution

Amendment I: Freedom of Religion, Speech, Press, Petition, and
                 Assembly (ratified 1791)
Amendment II: Right to Bear Arms (ratified 1791)
Amendment III: Quartering of Soldiers (ratified 1791)
Amendment IV: Freedom from Unfair Search and Seizures
                 (ratified 1791)
Amendment V: Right to Due Process (ratified 1791)
Amendment VI: Rights of the Accused (ratified 1791)
Amendment VII: Right to Trial by Jury (ratified 1791)
Amendment VIII: Freedom from Cruel and Unusual Punishment
                 (ratified 1791)
Amendment IX: Construction of the Constitution (ratified 1791)
Amendment X: Powers of the States and People (ratified 1791)
Amendment XI: Judicial Limits (ratified 1795)
Amendment XII: Presidential Election Process (ratified 1804)
Amendment XIII: Abolishing Slavery (ratified 1865)
Amendment XIV: Equal Protection, Due Process, Citizenship for All
                 (ratified 1868)

The Amendments to the U.S. Constitution

Amendment XV: Race and the Right to Vote (ratified 1870)
Amendment XVI: Allowing Federal Income Tax (ratified 1913)
Amendment XVII: Establishing Election to the U.S. Senate
                   (ratified 1913)
Amendment XVIII: Prohibition (ratified 1919)
Amendment XIX: Granting Women the Right to Vote (ratified 1920)
Amendment XX: Establishing Term Commencement for Congress
                   and the President (ratified 1933)
Amendment XXI: Repeal of Prohibition (ratified 1933)
Amendment XXII: Establishing Term Limits for U.S. President
                   (ratified 1951)
Amendment XXIII: Allowing Washington, D.C., Representation in the
                   Electoral College (ratified 1961)
Amendment XXIV: Prohibition of the Poll Tax (ratified 1964)
Amendment XXV: Presidential Disability and Succession
                   (ratified 1967)
Amendment XXVI: Lowering the Voting Age (ratified 1971)
Amendment XXVII: Limiting Congressional Pay Increases
                   (ratified 1992)

Appendix B

Court Cases Relevant to the Fifteenth Amendment

Scott v. Sandford, 1857

In this case, usually referred to as the Dred Scott decision, the Supreme Court ruled that a free black man whose parents were slaves was not a full citizen under the terms of the U.S. Constitution. The decision was soon judged a mistake and was a major inspiration for the Fifteenth as well as the Thirteenth and Fourteenth Amendments.

Plessy v. Ferguson, 1896

In this case the Supreme Court determined racial segregation was not unconstitutional and that the states, therefore, had the right to establish institutions that were "separate but equal." The decision provided for an era of "Jim Crow" laws in which blacks were forbidden to join whites in contexts as varied as buses and lunch counters.

Giles v. Harris, 1903

The Supreme Court held in this decision that the State of Alabama was not obligated to register African Americans to vote under current state rules that placed a variety of barriers in the way of registration, such as citizenship tests. The Court's rationale was that the plaintiff's complaint was not egregious enough for it to interfere in what was ultimately a matter for states and local governments.

Nixon v. Herndon, 1927

In this case, which laid the basis for later decisions such as *Grovey v. Townsend* and *Smith v. Allwright*, the Supreme Court determined that the State of Texas could not forbid African Americans to vote in local Democratic Party primaries. It helped to bring about the end of all-white primaries in other states as well.

Terry v. Adams, 1953

In this case the Supreme Court determined that because of the Fifteenth Amendment guarantees a Texas organization known as the Jaybird Association, which operated like a political party and held primaries, could not limit its membership to white people, as it had since its founding in 1889.

Brown v. Board of Education, 1954

This decision overturned the 1896 *Plessy v. Ferguson* decision. It held that the establishment of separate schools for white and African American children was a violation of constitutional rights. The decision set a precedent for the overturning of other segregationary laws and was an inspiration for civil rights and African American groups to assert their right to vote everywhere under the Fifteenth Amendment.

Oregon v. Mitchell, 1970

In this case, the Supreme Court determined that it was constitutional to ban the literacy tests that some states had used to stop some people from voting. The Court argued that such tests tended to be based on racial discrimination and therefore violated the Fifteenth Amendment. The case also allowed voters to cast their ballots from the age of eighteen and banned the states from using state residency requirements to limit their voting for presidential or vice presidential electors. In all these the Court upheld measures contained in the 1965 Voting Rights Act.

City of Mobile (AL) v. Bolden, 1980

In this decision the Supreme Court held that the city of Mobile, Alabama, could continue to elect local officials using an at-large voting system. Local African Americans had charged that such a system had diluted the voting power of African Americans since they tended to be concentrated in certain areas, and a lower court had agreed that Mobile's at-large system was a violation of the Fifteenth Amendment's guarantees.

The Supreme Court reversed and remanded the decision on the basis that Mobile's African Americans could cast their ballots easily and without hindrance.

Rice v. Cayetano, 2000

This case concerned a trust in Hawaii that was charged with maintaining certain land use rights. The members of the trust were chosen in a statewide election in which only those who were deemed "Hawaiians" could vote. This legal classification consisted of people who were descended from the native inhabitants of the Hawaiian Islands as of 1778, which was the point when Americans, Europeans, and others began to settle in the islands. The plaintiff complained that, as a citizen of Hawaii but not a "Hawaiian," his right to vote was being denied him on the basis of race. The Supreme Court agreed.

Crawford v. Marion County Election Board, 2008

In this decision the Supreme Court upheld the right of the state of Indiana to require voters to present photo identification, a practice found in other states as well. Challengers argued that such a requirement threatened to disenfranchise the poor or minorities who might not have photo identification or be aware of the law. The Court held, however, that such a requirement was reasonable and did not violate the Constitution's voting rights guarantees.

For Further Research

Books

Akhil Reed Amar, *America's Constitution: A Biography*. New York: Random House, 2005.

Alfred Avins, ed., *The Reconstruction Amendments' Debates*. Richmond: The Virginia Commission on Constitutional Government, 1967.

Judith Baer, *Equality Under the Constitution*. Ithaca, NY: Cornell University Press, 1983.

John W. Blassingame and John R. McKivigan, eds., *The Frederick Douglass Papers, Series One: Speeches, Debates, and Interviews, Volume 4: 1864–1880*. New Haven, CT: Yale University Press, 1991.

William Brock, *An American Crisis: Congress and Reconstruction*. London: Macmillan, 1963.

W.E.B. Du Bois, *Black Reconstruction in America*. New York: Harcourt Brace, 1935.

Lee Epstein and Thomas G. Walker, *Constitutional Law for a Changing America: Rights Liberties, and Justice*. Washington, DC, Congressional Quarterly, 1992.

Adam Fairclough, *Better Day Coming: Blacks and Equality, 1890–2000*. New York: Viking, 2001.

George P. Fletcher, *Our Secret Constitution: How Lincoln Redefined American Democracy*. New York: Oxford University Press, 2001.

Eric Foner, *Forever Free: The Story of Emancipation and Reconstruction*. New York: Knopf, 2005.

———, *Nothing but Freedom: Emancipation and Its Legacy*. Baton Rouge: Louisiana State University Press, 1983.

Lawrence M. Friedman, *A History of American Law*. 3rd ed. New York: Touchstone, 2001.

Paul Goodman, *Of One Blood: Abolitionism and the Origins of Racial Equality*. Berkeley: University of California Press, 1998.

Kenneth L. Karst, *Belonging to America: Equal Citizenship and the Constitution*. New Haven, CT: Yale University Press, 1989.

Alexander Keyssar, *The Right to Vote: The Contested History of Democracy in the United States*. New York: Basic Books, 2001.

J. Morgan Kousser, *Colorblind Injustice: Minority Voting Rights and the Undoing of the Second Reconstruction*. Chapel Hill: University of North Carolina Press, 1999.

Brooks D. Simpson, *The Reconstruction Presidents*. Lawrence: University Press of Kansas, 1998.

Periodicals

Sarah A. Adams, "The Basic Right of Citizenship: A Comparative Study," Center for Immigration Studies, September 1993. www.cis.org/articles/1993/back793.html.

William Arp III and Belisha Morton, "A Political History and Analysis of Disenfranchisement and Restoration of the Black Vote in Louisiana," *Western Journal of Black Studies*, 2005.

Mike Baker, "Black Turnout Strong in Early Voting in South," *Huffington Post*, October 23, 2008. www.huffingtonpost.com.

Gabriel J. Chin, "Reconstruction, Felon Disenfranchisement, and the Right to Vote: Did the 15th Amendment Repeal Section 2 of the 14th Amendment?" *Georgetown Law Review*, January 2004.

Adam B. Cox and Thomas J. Miles, "Judging the Voting Rights Act," *Columbia Law Review*, January 2008.

Lani Guinier, "The Triumph of Tokenism: The Voting Rights Act and the Theory of Black Electoral Success," *Michigan Law Review*, 1991.

Jet, "Tennessee Becomes the Last State to Ratify the 15th Amendment," April 21, 1997.

Ellen D. Katz, "Race and the Right to Vote After *Rice v. Cayetano*," *Michigan Law Review*, December 2000.

Payton McRary, "How the Voting Rights Act Works: Implementation of a Civil Rights Policy 1965–2002," *South Carolina Law Review*, 2006.

Curtis Morgan, Mary Ellen Klas, and Charles Rabin, "Florida Counties Split over Voter Verification," *Miami Herald*, October 26, 2008.

Armistead L. Robinson, "Beyond the Realm of Social Consensus: New Meanings of Reconstruction for American History," *Journal of American History*, September 1981.

Mark Sherman, "Court Hears NC Minority Voting Rights Lawsuit," *San Jose (CA) Mercury News*, October 14, 2008.

Andrea Stone, "House Renews Voting Rights Act," *USA Today*, July 13, 2006.

Time, "Enforcing the 15th," March 26, 1965.

Yale Law Journal, "The Strange Career of 'State Action' Under the Fifteenth Amendment," July 1965.

Web Sites

Black Voting Rights: The Creation of the 15th Amendment, http://15thamendment.harpweek.com. This site presents a comprehensive look at the Fifteenth Amendment's background and history as well as its legacy as the source of African American suffrage. It includes a time line, glossary, and list of sources.

Fair Vote, www.fairvote.org. The Web site of an organization involved in political and legal efforts to ensure the right to vote for all. The site includes links to current news and controversies as well as information on other voting rights groups.

National Voting Rights Institute, www.nvri.org. The Web site of an organization seeking to ensure open and legal access to the right to vote. It offers links to relevant articles and current news.

The U.S. Constitution Online, www.usconstitution.net. This site provides a wide variety of resources about the Constitution, including explanations of all amendments.

Index